Fire and Rescue Service Manual

Volume 3
Fire Safety

Fire Safety Engineering – A Basic Guide for Fire Authority Enforcement

HM Fire Service Inspectorate Publications Section

London: TSO

Published by TSO (The Stationery Office) and available from:

Online
www.tso.co.uk/bookshop

Mail, Telephone, Fax & E-mail
TSO
PO Box 29, Norwich, NR3 1GN
Telephone orders/General enquiries: 0870 600 5522
Fax orders: 0870 600 5533
E-mail: book.orders@tso.co.uk
Textphone 0870 240 3701

TSO Shops
123 Kingsway, London, WC2B 6PQ
020 7242 6393 Fax 020 7242 6394
68-69 Bull Street, Birmingham B4 6AD
0121 236 9696 Fax 0121 236 9699
9-21 Princess Street, Manchester M60 8AS
0161 834 7201 Fax 0161 833 0634
16 Arthur Street, Belfast BT1 4GD
028 9023 8451 Fax 028 9023 5401
18-19 High Street, Cardiff CF10 1PT
029 2039 5548 Fax 029 2038 4347
71 Lothian Road, Edinburgh EH3 9AZ
0870 606 5566 Fax 0870 606 5588

TSO Accredited Agents
(see Yellow Pages)

and through good booksellers

Published with the permission of the Office of the Deputy Prime Minister
on behalf of the Controller of Her Majesty's Stationery Office

ISBN 0 11 341277 0

Printed in Great Britain on material containing 75% post-consumer waste and 25% ECF pulp.

Printed in the United Kingdom for The Stationery Office
N164133 C25 03/04 5673

Contents

Preface   vii

Chapter 1 – Introduction   1

Chapter 2 – Fire Safety Philosophy and Technique   9

2.1   The Philosophy of Fire Safety   9
2.2   Passive fire safety   9
2.3   Implications within Prescriptive Standards   11
2.4   Fire Safety Engineering   12

Chapter 3 – The Application of Fire Safety Engineering   13

3.1   Qualitative Design Review   13
3.2   Quantitative Analysis   14
3.3   Design fire scenario   16
3.4   Fire Safety Engineering Acceptance Criterion   16

Chapter 4 – Smoke control systems   19

4.1   Types of smoke control   19
4.2   Smoke & heat exhaust ventilation systems (SHEVS)   19
4.3   Application of SHEVS to buildings   20
4.4   Design of smoke reservoirs   21
4.5   Removal of hot smoke and gases   21
4.6   Smoke control using pressurisation   21

Chapter 5 – Suppression, Detection and
            Compartmentation   23

5.1   Sprinklers   23
5.2   Automatic fire detectors and fire warning systems   24
5.3   Compartmentation   25
5.4   Automatic systems   25

Chapter 6 – Means of escape in case of fire   27

6.1   General   27
6.2   Calculating escape times   27
6.3   Occupant characteristics   28
6.4   Hazard Assessment   28
6.5   Evacuation Strategy   28
6.6   Time between ignition and alarm   28

6.7	Probable time for escape	29
6.8	People at particular risk	29
6.9	Psychological effects	30
6.10	Evacuation of people with disabilities	30

Chapter 7 – Management and Fire-fighting — 33

7.1	Management	33
7.2	First aid fire-fighting	33
7.3	Fire service facilities	33

Chapter 8 – Fire safety enforcement — 35

8.1	General	35
8.2	General overview of scheme	35
8.3	Hazard assessment and design fire	36
8.4	Smoke control	38
8.5	Pressurisation	38
8.6	Smoke and heat exhaust ventilation systems (SHEVS)	38
8.7	Smoke reservoirs	39
8.8	Detection and activation	41
8.9	Compartmentation	41
8.10	Means of escape	41
8.11	Management	42
8.12	Fire-fighting access	42

Chapter 9 – Fire Safety Engineering checklist — 43

9.1	Introduction	43
9.2	General overview of scheme	43
9.3	Hazard assessment	44
9.4	Predicted/Design fire scenario	44
9.5	Conductive heat flux	44
9.6	Smoke and Heat Exhaust Ventilation Systems	44
9.7	Pressure Differential systems	45
9.8	Atria	45
9.9	Fire detection and alarm systems	45
9.10	Sprinkler and fire-fighting systems	46
9.11	Means of escape in case of fire	46
9.12	Fire-fighting access	47

Chapter 10 – Standardisation of Fire Safety Engineering at National, European and International Levels — 49

10.1	Introduction	49
10.2	British Standard BS 7974:2001	51
10.3	Structure of Code of Practice BS 7974:2001	52
10.4	Sub-system 1. Initiation and development of fire within the enclosure of origin	53
10.5	Sub-system 2. Spread of smoke and toxic gases within and beyond the enclosure of origin	54

10.6   Sub-system 3 (PD 7974-3:2003) Structural response and fire
        spread beyond the enclosure of origin   54
10.7   Sub-system 4 (PD 7974-4:2003) Detection of fire and activation
        of fire protection systems   54
10.8   Sub-system 5. Fire service intervention   55
10.9   Sub-system 7. Risk assessment, uncertainty and safety factors   55
10.10   Technical Reports BS ISO/TR 13387: Parts 1 to 8: 1999   55
10.11   SS1. Initiation and development of fire and fire effluents   56
10.12   SS2. Movement of fire effluents   56
10.13   SS3. Structural response and fire spread beyond the enclosure
        of origin   57
10.14   SS4. Detection, activation and suppression   57
10.15   SS5. Fire Service intervention   58
10.16   SS6. Life, health and safety of people   59
10.17   SS7. Property protection   59
10.18   SS8. Environmental protection   59

Chapter 11 – Technical Standards in support of
        Fire Safety Engineering   61

11.1   Introduction   61
11.2   Technical Standards   63
11.3   List of Technical Standards (Euronorms – ENs)   64
11.4   Fire Behaviour of Construction Products   64
11.5   Fire detection and alarm systems   65
11.6   Smoke and heat control systems   66
11.7   Fixed fire-fighting systems   66
11.8   Fixed fire-fighting systems. Components for gas extinguishing
        systems   66
11.9   Fixed fire-fighting systems. Powder systems   67
11.10   Fixed fire-fighting systems. Automatic sprinkler systems   67
11.11   Other, non-mandated technical standards   67
11.12   Portable fire extinguishers   68
11.13   Extended Application of Test Methods   68

Appendix 1 – Tables   69

Table 1   70
Notes to Table 1   71
Table 2   72
Notes to Table 2   73

Glossary of Terms   75

Acknowledgements   77

Preface

(1)   This Manual is intended as a guide for fire authorities who act as enforcement agencies for the fire safety regulations and orders; it is particularly aimed at those officers who may not be familiar with the application of fire safety engineering in building designs. It can be seen as a procedural document, setting out the key information which should be provided by applicants for building control or other approvals authorities.

(2)   This Manual describes the steps, which may be taken by the fire safety engineer when devising an engineered scheme for a building and, as appropriate, gives minimum or maximum criteria beyond which the validity of the design may be questionable.

(3)   To assist enforcers in determining schemes incorporating fire safety engineering, a checklist is provided. (See Chapter 9.)

(4)   It is recommended that enforcement agencies use the checklist to assist in evaluating fire safety engineering solutions submitted by applicants. The checklist, which ideally should accompany the application, will give enforcers ready access to key information, which can be compared with values quoted in this Manual.

(5)   This will enable enforcers to make a realistic assessment of the application and it's engineering solution, without necessarily having to validate the mathematics supporting the proposal in each and every case.

(6)   This Manual is not a prescriptive guide to fire engineering and therefore, should not be used by designers or engineers as an alternative to the methods of calculation recommended in British Standard BS 7974:2001. Whilst it is aimed at enforcing agencies, it may however, prove useful to designers and engineers by providing an outline of a typical fire safety engineering design.

(7)   The procedures described in this Manual take account of the existing consultation procedures between building control authorities and fire authorities as recommended in the Joint Procedural Guidance published by the Department of Transport, Local Government and the Regions and the Home Office. The standard form used for consultation by Approved Inspectors is also acknowledged.

(8)   The principal objective of fire engineering is that when a fire occurs, it will provide an environment that has a level of safety that is equal to or superior to the level that would be developed by direct compliance with what may be regarded as conventional and/or traditional requirements for fire safety.

(9)   There are many components of the fire safety environment, all of which can be designed, manufactured and installed in a building. All such components need to be supported by efficient and effective management of the building.

(10)   In circumstances where it is decided to use an engineered solution, generally it will be quickly realised that no one, single solution offers the required consideration. It is often therefore necessary to adjust the individual aspects of any considered solution until the closest 'fit' can be achieved. Such consideration will often require an evaluation of the engineering models being used.

(11)   It is generally accepted that there are no 'right' or 'wrong' models under such circumstances. Just because the model originally chosen did not give the required consideration does not mean it was the incorrect model. Therefore, in considering the acceptance of any fire engineered solution, if adjustments are to be made to render the design acceptable and such adjustment involved the change of any of the models used; this should not be regarded as an error in the initial approach.

(12)   The basic objective of either a prescriptive or engineered approach is the specification and acceptance of the life fire safety measures provided in the building.

Chapter 1 – Introduction

1.1 **British Standard BS 7974:2001** – *Application of fire safety engineering principles to the design of buildings – Code of Practice* defines fire safety enginering as "the application of scientific and engineering principles to the protection of people, property and the environment from fire". In practise, fire safety engineering involves the use of science based or statistical calculations to demonstrate an adequate level of fire safety for a specific building, structure or installation. Often it will be applied to a part of a project while other parts follow other standard guidance or codes.

1.2 British Standard BS 7974 therefore provides a framework for an engineering approach to fire safety which may be applied to both the design of new buildings and the appraisal of existing buildings, and to show that regulatory requirements can be, or are satisfied.

1.3 British Standard BS 7974 is also intended to provide a framework for a flexible, but formalised approach to fire safety design that can also be readily assessed by the approvals bodies.

1.4 However, in either of the above contexts, the use of BS 7974 assumes a level of knowledge that may not be available. The Foreword of BS 7974 clearly states that "It has been assumed in the drafting of this British Standard that the execution of its provisions is entrusted to appropriately qualified and competent people". For that reason, this Handbook offers a basic explanation of the principles of fire safety engineering in order to promote an understanding.

1.5 Fire safety engineering is also defined in the international and European fora as 'the application of engineering principles, rules and expert judgement based on a scientific appreciation of the fire phenomena, the effects of fire and of the reaction and behaviour of people, in order:

(i)   To save life, protect property and preserve the environment and heritage;
(ii)   To quantify the hazards and fire occurrence and development and its effects;
(iii) To evaluate the optimum protective and preventative measures necessary to limit, within prescribed levels, the consequences of fire'.

1.6 With no agreed universal definition available, at this time, the definition given in the British Standard Code of Practice is given preference here. However, from both these definitions flows the definition of **Fire Safety Engineer** as a 'person suitably qualified and experienced in fire safety engineering'.

1.7   This is important as already stated. The Foreword of BS 7974 makes the assumption that the execution of its provisions will be entrusted to appropriately qualified and competent people. This applies to both design fire engineers and those responsible for approving the designs and calculations as part of a building regulation approval or risk assessment of an existing building.

1.8   Fire safety engineering may be considered under several headings:

- The *process* of fire safety engineering is about measurements and relationships, backed by scientific study, for engineering application to the problems, but where experience and judgement can contribute, as in many other engineering disciplines.
- The *context* of fire safety engineering is the need to evaluate fire hazard and risk and to offer fire safety strategies and designs based on performance not prescription.
- The *tools* supporting fire safety engineering are the calculation methods (models), that describe the measurements, relationships and interactions and any necessary test results.
- The *inputs* are the physical data for the calculation methods, derived from measurement methods or tests.
- The *framework* of fire safety engineering basically comprises the essential core, and transfer of knowledge, which permits an engineering approach and the education and training of users.

1.9   Fire safety engineering is usually carried out in response to the requirements of regulations such as Building Regulations, Fire Regulations etc., the fire safety aspects of the International Maritime Organisation (IMO) for safety of ships. Alternatively, it may be offered as a way of satisfying insurance conditions or as a means of protecting irreplaceable buildings or artefacts.

1.10   The choice usually offered to the building control authorities is often quite simple – perhaps along the lines of 'If I provide that and do this, can I do that?' The inter-linking of such provisions may be an integral part of the proposed building design and may depend upon the effective and efficient management of the building.

1.11   With the introduction over the last ten years of legislation such as the Construction Design and Management Regulations 1994 and the Fire Precautions (Workplace) Regulations 1997, as amended, it has now become more acceptable to involve continuing management of risks and maintenance of life safety installations such as smoke vents, alarm systems etc.

1.12   However, fire safety engineering is still seen as a relatively new concept, which can be used as an alternative to traditional prescriptive methods of fire safety.

Fire safety engineering involves the use of measurements backed by scientific study and the use of experience and judgement, as in other forms of engineering disciplines. In this context, fire safety engineering evaluates the fire hazard and risk and involves fire strategies and designs based on performance rather than prescription. The essential tools of fire safety engineering are the calculation methods, using inputs from physical data. From this data, the outputs from a given fire scenario can be calculated and the means of meeting the fire safety objectives determined.

1.13   The methodology used in fire safety engineering is set out in British Standard 7974: 2001 and in BS ISO/TR 13387: 1999. At the time of writing, BS 7974 was still being developed, but sufficient data is available to allow architects and designers to reach realistic conclusions in the design of buildings using fire safety engineering techniques.

1.14   British Standard 7974: 2001 is supported by a number of parts or published documents (as yet incomplete), each giving advice on matters that must be taken into account in the design of all fire engineering schemes. These will be:

Part 0. Guide to the design framework and fire safety engineering procedures.
Part 1. Initiation and development of fire within the enclosure of origin.
Part 2. Spread of smoke and toxic gases within and beyond the enclosure of origin.
Part 3. Structural response and fire spread beyond the enclosure of origin.
Part 4. Detection of fire and activation of fire protection systems.
Part 5. Fire service intervention.
Part 6. Evacuation*.
Part 7. Probabilistic fire risk assessment.

* Yet to be finalised by the BS Technical Committee FSH/24.

1.15   Further information of fire safety engineering methods giving a slightly different approach, can be found in BS ISO/TR 13387, which is divided into eight parts as follows:

Part 1. Application of fire performance concepts to design objectives.
Part 2. Commentary on the equations given in Part 1.
Part 3. Assessment and verification of mathematical fire models.
Part 4. Initiation and development of fire and generation of fire effluents.
Part 5. Movement of fire effluents
Part 6. Structural response and fire spread beyond the enclosure of origin.
Part 7. Detection, activation and suppression
Part 8. Life safety – Occupant behaviour, location and condition.

1.16   The lists above demonstrate the complexities involved in using fire safety engineering in building design. The problem is exacerbated by the fact that very little precise information is available on the performance of combustible materials in fires in a range of building uses. The fire safety engineer has to use professional judgment in evaluation the design fire scenario and its probable effects on people and buildings.

1.17 Fire safety engineering can be applied to a range of building designs and uses. The engineering solution should be clearly identified in the strategy report and may involve active systems to support passive systems and involve their management. For example, buildings incorporating atria normally require some form of control to prevent the atrium void creating unacceptable levels of smoke and heat spread. Specific advice on the design of fire safety in atria can be found in British Standard 5588: Part7: 1988 – soon to be replaced by the appropriate part of the British Standard 9999 series.

1.18 Smoke and heat exhaust ventilation techniques are often used to control the spread of smoke and heat in large buildings. Advice on the design of smoke and heat ventilation systems can be found in British Standards BS 7346 and BS EN 12101, as well as the Building Research Establishment publications and the CIBSE guide to part 'E'.

1.19 The activation of smoke control systems is normally through the use of fire detection and alarm equipment. British Standard 5839 – Fire Detection and alarms systems for buildings: Parts 1–9 (see below) and the many parts of BS EN 54, gives advice on the design and installation of fire detection and alarm systems.

British Standard BS 5839 – Fire detection and alarm systems for buildings:

(i)   Part 1 – Code of practice for system design, installation and servicing;
(ii)   Part 2 – Specification for manual call points;
(iii)   Part 3 – Specification for automatic release mechanisms for certain fire protection equipment;
(iv)   Part 4 – Specification for control and indicating equipment;
(v)   Part 5 – Specification for optical beam smoke detectors;
(vi)   Part 6 – Code of practice for the design and installation of fire detection and fire alarm systems in dwellings;
(vii)   Part 8 – Code of practice for the design, installation and servicing of voice alarm systems.
(ix)   Part 9 – Code of Practice for the design, installation, commissoning and maintenance of emergency voice communication systems.

(Note – Part 7 has not yet been published)

1.20 Automatic sprinkler systems are often used as a means of controlling fires to within their design parameters. Advice on automatic sprinkler and other water based suppression systems can be found in British Standard 5306 – Fire extinguishing installations and equipment on premises; Parts 1–7 (see below) and BS EN 12845.

British Standard BS 5306 – Fire extinguishing installations and equipment on premises:

(i)	Part 0	Guide for the selection of installed systems and other fire equipment;
(ii)	Part 1	Hydrant systems, hose reels and foam inlets;
(iii)	Part 2	Specification for sprinkler systems;
(iv)	Part 3	Code of practice for selection, installation and maintenance of portable fire extinguishers;
(v)	Part 4	Specification for carbon dioxide systems;
(vi)	Part 5	Halon systems;
	Part 5–1	Specification for Halon 1301 total flooding;
	Part 5–2	Halon 1211 total flooding systems;
(vii)	Part 6	Foam systems;
	Part 6–1	Specification for low expansion foam systems;
	Part 6–2	Specification for medium and high expansion foam systems;
(viii)	Part 7	Specification for powder systems.

1.21   Proposals using fire safety engineering can place an enormous burden on the fire services. This manual is intended as a guide for fire safety enforcers to assist them in determining the validity of schemes incorporating fire engineering. It can also be seen as a procedural document, setting out the key information, which should be, provided by applicants for Building Regulation or other approvals authorities regarding fire safety engineering designs. These procedures will enable fire safety enforcers to make an assessment of the application and its engineering without necessarily having to validate the mathematics and/or calculations supporting the proposal.

1.22   This procedure takes account of consultation procedures already existing between building authorities and fire authorities as recommended in the joint procedural guide published by the Department for Transport, the Regions and Local Government and the Home Office. The Standard Form used for consultation by Approved Inspectors is also acknowledged.

1.23   For the purposes of this document and the discussion contained therein, an understanding of certain terminology must be clearly held. Some related terms and definitions are provided in the Glossary of Terms. Without such an understanding, confusion is likely as the terms are widely used in any discussion on fire safety engineering. Some comments on the different types of Regulations follow.

1.24   **Prescriptive regulations:** These are Regulations such as the early version of the United Kingdom Building Regulations (the 1965, 1972 and 1976 Regulations were of this type), that achieve their fire safety objectives, and/or components of these objectives, by specifying what has to be provided. In some cases, these may be on the basis of performance requirements – fire resistance test performance, reaction to fire performance. However, they will be on the basis of requirements given in physical terms, e.g. maximum building height, maximum compartment size(s) etc., that are dependent upon the intended use of the building. In such cases, the fire safety objectives are usually explicit, and deviation from the regulatory prescription required generally some compensating protection measures in the form of relaxation or derogation of the basic requirements.

1.25   **Performance based regulations:** These are regulations that specify explicitly their objectives and/or the components of these objectives, in terms of quantifiable criteria that have to be satisfied. In England and Wales, this major philosophical development took place with the Building Act 1984 and the 1985 Building Regulations.

1.26   Specifically, the England and Wales Regulation 'B1' contains the wording *'The building shall be designed and constructed so that there are appropriate provisions for the early warning of fire and appropriate means of escape in case of fire from the building to a place of safety outside the building capable of being safely and effectively used at all times.'*

1.27   This type of expression allows a wide variety of interpretations of the word *'appropriate'*. It also allows the possibility of compensating for a deficiency in one element of the means of escape with an extra provision in another element.

1.28   The functional nature of the requirements of the England and Wales (Approved Document B) and Northern Ireland regulations (Technical Booklet E) is emphasised in the following paragraphs which statements are taken directly from the two publications.

1.29   'The Approved Documents are intended to provide guidance for some of the more common building situations. However, there may well be alternative ways of achieving compliance with the requirements. Thus, there is no obligation to adopt any particular solution contained in an Approved Document if you prefer to meet the relevant requirement in some other way. (Approved Document B)'; and

1.30   'There is no obligation to follow the methods or comply with the standards set out in this Technical Booklet. If you prefer you may adopt another way of meeting the requirements of the Building Regulations but you will have to demonstrate that you have satisfied those requirements by other means.' (Northern Ireland Technical Booklet E).

1.31   The Scottish Regulations do not allow variations of the 'deemed to satisfy' provisions contained in technical standards but rely on a relaxation procedure where a design does not meet the standard guidance. They require the applicant for a building warrant to make a formal application to the local authority for a relaxation if they propose a solution not contained in the Technical Booklet. If the relaxation is refused the applicant can appeal to the Scottish Executive.

1.32   Therefore, Building Control in the UK outside Scotland has introduced the concept of functional requirements. From 1985 the levels of safety to be achieved were given for the first time in functional terms, i.e. the levels to be achieved was given, but the actual method of achieving the level was not prescribed. This allowed Architects, Developers and users a far greater freedom in their designs, applications and use of the building.

1.33　Paragraph 0.11 of Approved Document 'B' goes further in acknowledging that a fire engineering approach may be the *only* practical way to achieving a satisfactory standard of fire safety in some large and complex buildings. Similarly, it also notes that fire safety engineering may also be suitable for solving a problem with an aspect of the building design which otherwise follows the provisions of the Approved Document 'B' or existing buildings of special architectural or historic interest.

1.34　Within the General Introduction on Fire Safety, the Building Regulations, Approved Document 'B' Fire Safety acknowledges that some variation of the provisions set out in the document may also be appropriate for application to existing buildings and particularly in buildings of special architectural or historic interest. In such cases, adherence to the guidance given in Approved Document 'B' could prove unduly restrictive.

1.35　In such cases, paragraph 0.12 of Approved Document 'B' suggests that it might be appropriate to take into account a range of safety measures, some of which are not dealt with in the Approved Document. These measures should be assessed against the hazard and risk peculiar to the particular case being considered.

1.36　Such an approach opens up the facility to consider detailed fire safety engineered solutions, Approved Document 'B' suggests that factors to be considered in any such provision might include:

(i)　The anticipated probability of a fire occurring;
(ii)　The anticipated fire severity;
(iii)　The ability of a structure to resist the spread of fire and smoke;
(iv)　The consequential danger to people in and around the building.

1.37　There are a wide variety of other measures that could also be considered to a greater or lesser extent, as appropriate in the circumstances. These could include:

(i)　The adequacy of means to prevent fire;
(ii)　The standard of means of escape;
(iii)　The provision of smoke control;
(iv)　The adequacy of the structure to resist the effects of fire;
(v)　The degree of fire containment;
(vi)　Fire separation between buildings or parts of buildings;
(vii)　The standard of active measures for fire extinguishment or control;
(viii)　Facilities to assist the fire service;
(ix)　Availability of powers to require staff training, e.g. under the Fire Precautions Act 1971, the Fire Precautions (Workplace) Regulations 1997, as amended, or registration or licensing procedures.

1.38 It is possible to use quantitative techniques (see section 2) to evaluate risk and hazard. Some factors in the measures listed above can give numerical values in some circumstances. The assumptions made when quantitative methods are used need careful assessment.

1.39 From the above it can be concluded that current building regulations in the UK acknowledge the role of fire engineering as a useful tool which can provide alternative approaches to fire safety than those in published guidance, although in Scotland such engineered solutions are likely to be the subject of a formal relaxation process. Professional staff from building control bodies and fire authorities will need the skills and experience to check building designs which involve fire engineering.

1.40 Within these performance-based regulations, it is necessary to differentiate between:

(i) **Performance-based requirements for products** – under standard conditions, it is generally the case for specific requirements for reaction to fire or fire resistance of individual products. The level of performance to be achieved (or provided) under the standard fire exposure conditions for fire resistance. This leaves the architect or designer the freedom to choose the product he wants. It would be unusual for such an approach to consider the possible synergy (interaction) between systems and/or products.

(ii) **Performance-based requirements for the entire building** – considering explicit fire safety objectives in terms of quantifiable criteria that need to be satisfied, e.g. in terms of maximum tenable conditions or time of escape of people or other functional requirements. The assessment of the fire safety level of the building is made using fire safety engineering tools and so considers the possible synergy between products.

1.41 **Functional regulations** These are regulations that specify what has to be achieved in terms of qualitative fire safety objectives. They do not specify how or what level of satisfaction has to be achieved and will usually be written in such terms as 'means shall be provided to prevent the spread of fire within the building over building surfaces'. The designer is therefore at liberty to choose whatever wall, ceiling or floor lining he wishes and his decision will be part of the overall data considered in the Qualitative Design Review.

1.42 **Deemed to satisfy** These are provisions within a regulation that is met by a specified solution without the need to provide supporting technical information. It is basically the acceptance of a particular form of construction that has been declared satisfactory without the need for any further testing.

Chapter 2 – Fire Safety Philosophy and Technique

2.1 The Philosophy of Fire Safety

2.1.1 Fire is a dynamic event which, if unchecked can grow from very small beginnings into a life threatening highly destructive conflagration. The life cycle of a fire passes through several stages, which can be expressed chronologically.

2.1.2 In the case of fires in buildings, there are limits of tolerability for the survival of people and of the building structure exposed to the fire. These may be expressed as:

(i) Life safety – the time available for escape;
(ii) Structural stability – the time before collapse.

2.1.3 The act of escaping from a fire is also a dynamic event and this too can be expressed in terms of time, i.e. the time required for escape.

2.1.4 The aim of fire safety, whether engineered or passive, must, therefore, be to ensure that people have sufficient time to escape, before the fire grows to life-threatening proportions and before the stability of the building is put at risk. The time *available* for escape must always be longer than the time *required* for escape.

2.1.5 In passive fire safety this is achieved by limiting the distance people may have to travel to reach a storey exit and by protecting vulnerable exit routes.

2.1.6 Fire safety engineering typically uses smoke control systems to keep exit routes clear of heat and smoke. Additionally, suppression systems may be incorporated into the scheme to give added means of escape time (life safety) and/or to protect firefighters together with associated protection of the structure and contents. Where these two systems are operating in the same building, they should be designed and installed to that they are able to work at their optimum capabilities and not reduce the effectiveness of each other.

2.2 Passive fire safety

2.2.1 Buildings using fire safety engineering should provide a standard of fire safety at least equivalent to those built to traditional passive standards. To achieve this it is helpful to understand the principles of passive standards and the implications within them.

2.2.2   Passive fire safety describes the practice of installing in buildings, non-active measures to increase the time available for escape and facilities to reduce the time required for escape. These include measures to ensure the integrity of the building structure whilst persons escape from fire.

2.2.3   The principles from which passive fire safety standards are derived are not necessarily based on scientific study but from judgements made by experts from information about fires. The standard tests on materials, e.g. doors, glazing etc., used have been modified over the years but not altered radically.

2.2.4   For the most part these standards are effective but provide for a high degree of redundancy, advocating levels of safety that are often higher than actual needs. However, they can fall short of actual needs and users should be aware of the shortcomings of some passive standards in certain circumstances. These include large shops displaying quantities of flammable materials likely to give rise to rapid fire spread and the possibility of extended escape times where people are committed to an activity, e.g. eating a meal, which causes them to be reluctant to leave the building. The basic requirement is that people should be able to move away from the fire, via a protected escape route remains.

2.2.5   Passive standards accept that people may have to move in smoke for controlled distances. For instance, office corridors providing two ways of escape are not required to have smoke stop doors from adjoining offices. This means that the corridor can become smoke logged from a fire in an adjoining room venting through a open door. The engineered solution should seek to avoid people having to move through heavily smoke contaminated areas or being subjected to excessive heat.

2.2.6   Levels of passive fire safety are normally prescribed in codes or guides. They include limiting the length of escape routes, protection of vulnerable escape routes to given values of fire resistance and the protection of vital elements of construction, again to prescribed levels of fire protection.

2.2.7   The limitation of the length of escape routes follows concepts advocated following studies of fires in Britain during the 1940s (Post War Building Studies). These suggested that means of escape should be time based, the times allocated varied according to the construction (not the contents) of a building, i.e.:

(i)   Constructed of combustible materials – 2 minutes.
(ii)   Incombustible structure with timber floors – $2^1/_2$ minutes.
(iii)   Totally incombustible structure – 3 minutes.

To these times were applied an average speed of travel (12 metres per minute) which gave the original travel distances.

2.2.8   In modern guides these distances have been varied to suit different uses of building, the concept of constructional difference being dropped. Rounding up during conversion from imperial to metric measurements and general increases of 50% to represent "indirect" travel distances have distorted the original thinking, but the principles behind those early concepts remain.

2.2.9 Many prescriptive guides using passive fire safety standards use risk classification according to the use of the building. These risk classifications are applied generically across the whole of the building to vary travel distances and other passive fire safety measures. They are often based on the likelihood of fire in a particular process or use, the probable rate of fire spread and the ultimate size of a fully developed fire in a particular class of building. Few, if any, of those risk classifications consider the specific risk to people in the building at the time of a fire. Consequently, these risk classifications are often not suitable as a risk assessment and should not be relied on to support an engineered solution.

2.3 Implications within Prescriptive Standards

2.3.1 Within the recommendations of prescriptive guidance are hidden implications. It is important that these implied standards are acknowledged in engineered solutions if equivalency is to be achieved.

2.3.2 In situations where alternative escape routes are provided, the travel distance to the nearest storey exit is prescribed, e.g. 45 metres. Therefore, by implication, the distance to the next nearest exit is also given. For example, where storey exits are at opposite ends of an office corridor, the exits will be 90 metres apart.

2.3.3 Where standards of safety are based on the availability of alternative escape routes, there is an implied assumption that the time available for escape will be sufficient for persons unable to use the nearest exit to reach the next nearest exit. In the example above, people unable to use the nearest exit may have to travel up to a total distance of 90 metres to the next nearest alternative. All of that distance could be in smoke. Exit routes are generally considered as alternative routes if the angle between them is at least 45°. In these cases, the maximum distance to the next nearest exit can be calculated by triangulation.

2.3.4 Research shows that the travel speed of 12 metres per minute used in prescriptive guides as well as engineered solutions, is the average speed for persons using a single unit exit door (760mm) in a single file or when negotiating stairs. Tests have shown that people can travel much faster than 12 metres per minute and that horizontal speeds will vary according to circumstances. For instance, on railway stations people can travel up to 90 metres per minute. Other problems which will affect the ease of escape may arise later, particularly when large numbers of people approach an exit together.

2.3.5 Travel speeds will not necessarily indicate the actual time people may take to travel to a storey exit after the alarm of fire has been given. Allowance must be made for a pre-action time, which is the interval between the alarm being given and the person actually starting their escape. Pre-action times will vary according to a person's familiarity with the building, their commitment at the time an alarm of fire is given and the quality of information given with the alarm. Verbal messages are often better than simple audible signals. Where pre-action times are likely to be longer, e.g. in hotels, this is compensated for by using shorter travel distances.

2.4   Fire Safety Engineering

2.4.1   The term fire safety engineering can be applied to any fire safety concept that relies on active systems designed to meet calculated objectives. Those objectives may be:

(i)   Life safety and the protection of means of escape routes.
(ii)   The protection of the building and its contents.
(iii)   The control of a fire to reduce its effects on the structure.

2.4.2   Fire engineering, safety standards are calculated to take into account all building features and management principles. Also considered, as appropriate, is the behaviour of people using them in a fire situation. The advantage of this approach is that the physical limitations on building design imposed by prescriptive fire safety standards can be largely overcome, giving greater scope for architects to design buildings to meet client needs.

2.4.3   In life safety applications, fire safety engineering is used to maintain a life supporting environment on exit routes. This is designed to keep exit routes clear of fire, heat and smoke for sufficient time to allow persons to leave the building and, where appropriate, fire-fighting access. A sound fire safety engineering solution would incorporate a number of the following components in its fire safety strategy:

(i)   Passive systems would include compartmentation;
(ii)   Active systems, e.g. smoke control systems/suppression systems/automatic fire detection and fire alarm systems management systems would include risk analysis and maintenance.
(iii)   Human behaviour criteria would include means of escape strategy, design fire assumptions and its potential growth and spread rates.

2.4.4   To ensure the capacity of a developing fire does not overwhelm engineering solution, it is common to include some form of fire control such as sprinklers or compartmentation. In other circumstances where the fire growth rate and final heat outputs can be expected to be low, suppression systems may not included in the scheme.

Chapter 3 – The Application of Fire Safety Engineering

3.1 Qualitative Design Review

3.1.1   At the early stages of the building design process, the proposal will be subjected to a qualitative design review (QDR). QDR is a technique in which the impact of possible fire hazards on the need to maintain the risk to people or the building structure to an acceptable level can be determined. The design needs of the proposal can then be assessed quantitatively against the design objectives of the designer. Any change in the design throughout the process needs to be agreed with the QDR team.

3.1.2   The QDR team on a major project might include the following:

(i)   Fire Safety Engineer.
(ii)   Architect.
(iii)   Services Engineer.
(iv)   Structural Engineer;
(v)   Member of operational management.
(vi)   Member of Approvals Agency and/or Insurer.

3.1.3   The QDR should take into account of:

(i)   The use of the building.
(ii)   The number and characteristics of proposed occupants (life safety schemes).
(iii)   The architectural design of the building.
(iv)   The fire safety objectives.
(v)   The fire hazards and possible consequences.
(vi)   Results of trial fire safety designs.
(vii)   Possible fire scenarios for analysis.
(viii) Proposed acceptance criteria.

3.1.4   The outcome of the QDR will determine the viability of the proposed scheme. Where viability cannot be established, the review should re-address the matters considered until either a satisfactory result is reached or the range of options within the original specification is exhausted. It should be ensured that only realistic data is used and that the results of trial fire safety designs or fire scenario predictions are not distorted to meet other objectives or constraints.

3.1.5   The QDR provides a largely qualitative set of outputs, which form the basis for the quantified analysis. The satisfactory completion of the QDR should typically provide the following information:

(i)   The results of the architectural review;
(ii)   A clear statement of the fire safety objectives;
(iii)   Identification of the significant hazards and their possible consequences;
(iv)   Evaluation of one or more of the trial designs;
(v)   The acceptance criteria and suggested methods of analysis;
(vi)   The specifications of the fire scenarios for analysis.

3.1.6   Following this review, it should be possible to decide which trial design is likely to be the optimum. At this stage, it should be possible to decide whether quantitative analysis is necessary to demonstrate that the design meets the fire safety objectives.

3.2   Quantitative Analysis

3.2.1   Following a Qualitative Design Review (QDR), it may be necessary to complete a Quantitative analysis. This analysis may be divided into a number of parts and each of these parts is covered by the sub-systems to be provided in the series of Published Documents that will eventually accompany BS 7974.

3.2.2   In order that a satisfactory quantification study can be undertaken, the trial fire safety design should consider the following:

(i)   Automatic suppression
(ii)   Detection.
(iii)   Compartmentation.
(iv)   Automatic systems.
(v)   Smoke control.
(vi)   Alarm and warning systems.
(vii)   Evacuation strategy.
(viii)   Means of escape.
(ix)   First aid fire-fighting.
(x)   Fire service facilities.
(xi)   Management of fire safety.
(xii)   Use of materials in a potential fire area.
(xiii)   The general configuration of materials.

3.2.3   These sub-systems are intended to provide guidance on the type of calculations that may be carried out in support of a fire engineering study and to present the general principles and procedures appropriate to the aspect of fire safety engineering covered by that part of the analysis. The sub-systems may each be used in isolation when analysing a particular aspect of design or all six sub-systems may be used together as part of an overall fire engineering evaluation of a building.

3.2.4   The various aspects of the analysis (or in effect each sub-system) may be quantified by either deterministic studies; or a probabilistic risk assessment.

3.2.5   In practice, the analysis may be an amalgam of some deterministic elements and some probabilistic elements. Deterministic models are based on physical, chemical, thermodynamic and human behavioural relationships, derived from scientific theories and empirical calculations. The alternative strategy is to treat fire as a series of random events and assess the possible outcome in a probabilistic manner in order to estimate the likelihood of a particular, unwanted event occurring.

3.2.6   Deterministic procedures quantify fire growth, fire spread, smoke movement and the consequences of these for the building and its occupants. A deterministic analysis also involves the evaluation of a set of circumstances that will provide a single outcome, i.e. whether the design will either be successful or not.

3.2.7   Several techniques are available for evaluating the development and effects of fire and the movement of people. Some of these techniques are described in the series of Published Documents that accompany BS 7974.

3.2.8   The interaction of fire, buildings and people can give rise to a very complex system. In order to evaluate fire safety in large complex buildings by deterministic calculations some conservative simplifications should be made. In theory several factors may contribute to the fire scenarios, but in practice the contribution of many factors will be insignificant.

3.2.9   By carefully selecting when and where to apply calculations and then adopting the calculation technique appropriate to the particular problem being considered, a more flexible, pragmatic and equally safe solution may be reached. Guidance on the selection of significant scenarios and initial assumptions is given in BS 7974: Published Document; Part 0.

3.2.10   When considering scenarios in isolation, the worst credible conditions for assigning values to the variables should always be chosen. However, it should be recognised that when considering several scenarios, using a series of unlikely events leads to an over-conservative design. On the other hand, using average values for the variables does not lead to a design that is likely to provide an acceptable level of safety.

3.2.11   The key to a successful analysis relies upon rationalising the problem quantitatively, in the context of the particular fire safety requirements, during the QDR. Attention may then be focused on the quantitative interpretation of the design and in particular the uncertainties that the quantification may involve.

3.3 Design fire scenario

3.3.1　A fire is an exothermic reaction caused when heat comes into contact with a flammable material. Except in the case where a material is volatile at normal temperatures, e.g. petrol, the application of heat causes the flammable substance to give off a flammable vapour, which, in the presence of sufficient heat is ignited. The heat from the fire then causes further vapours to be given off thus sustaining the fire until either it is extinguished or all of the fuel is consumed.

3.3.2　The fire will create a convective plume rising above it. In the main the plume will be air, drawn into the fire by the convective process and heated. It will also contain oxygen-depleted air and products from the combustion process, e.g. smoke. The mass of the convective plume (mass flux) will be proportional to the temperature of the fire and the area of its base.

3.3.3　As the plume rises, it will expand as it mixes with any additional air. The plume will also cool as it rises further from the fire. If the rising column comes against a horizontal surface, it will spread horizontally in all directions. This is known as a ceiling jet. The temperature of the plume or ceiling jet at any point will be according to the temperature of the fire and its height from the fire. Eventually the plume will dissipate into the atmosphere, the heavier products of combustion falling back to ground.

3.3.4　When designing a ventilation scheme, the designer will take into account the flammability of fuel sources likely to be involved in fire and their probable rate of heat release. From this a fire scenario (design fire) will be assumed from which the temperature of a steady state fire and the mass flux can be calculated. The ventilation system will be designed to accommodate those values

3.3.5　For similar fuel sources, the intensity of a fire is usually directly proportional to the amount of oxygen present. Ventilated fires always have a plentiful supply of oxygen due to the inflow of replacement air. The ability of that air to reach the fire will depend on the configuration of the burning fuel. For instance, stacked chairs will burn vigorously because the air can get into the fire from all sides and under the fuel. Fires against walls deny access to air on the wall side, whilst fires in the corner between two walls denies access on two sides. This results in a greater flame length up the wall.

3.4 Fire Safety Engineering Acceptance Criterion

3.4.1　As has already been stated, fire safety engineering offers a legitimate, alternative approach to the present system of building control. The aim is to achieve a satisfactory level of safety (acceptance of risk) in a building.

3.4.2　There can be no suggestion, in such a solution, that the existing codes are inadequate and that the engineered solution being offered is the only 'correct' procedure.

3.4.3 The accepted principle here is that the developer/designer of the building wished to express themselves conceptually, but were unable to do so using either the generally accepted design criteria or restrictions placed on the use of any specific construction material. The 'adjustment' of certain design or construction principles therefore is intended to allow the original concept to be achieved.

3.4.4 A fire-engineered solution would normally be considered during the planning/design stages of any building or structure. Indeed, this may be one of the first considerations to be given to the actual detail because it may have been determined at the conceptual stage that the innovative approach being adopted will not fit the more traditional or conventional techniques.

3.4.5 It will be at this early stage that the fire engineering consideration and evaluation given to the desired design parameters, will enable adjustments to be made, whilst perhaps maintaining the integrity of the original design. As with all engineering studies it will be necessary to take account of all the possible variations, before coming to an agreed position.

3.4.6 In considering the acceptability, or otherwise of an engineered solution, a number of basic parameters must be considered. These usually concentrate on the 'acceptability' or otherwise of the risk. There may be a number of valid reasons as to why a 'risk' may be acceptable these would include:

(i) **Ignorance** – if the existence of the risk is unknown or not fully understood, it may be accepted for many years. An example of this may be the fire behaviour of certain construction products, e.g. large insulating (sandwich) panels. In such cases when the risk became apparent, action was taken to reduce the risk.

(ii) **Negligible** – if the risk is so low that they can be considered negligible they often can be accepted. However, the difficulty here is to define 'negligible'.

3.4.7 If the risk identified is considered to be above what would be classed as 'negligible' then two further classifications may be applied. The increased level of risk (above that considered negligible) is either considered tolerable or intolerable.

(iii) **Tolerable** – any high, medium or low risk is usually considered tolerable when the benefits of the situation causing the risk are considered to outweigh the level of risk. For example, there are risks inherent in travel by air, but there is universal acceptance that the advantages of such mode of travel far outweigh any perceived level of risk. Such acceptance relies upon a simple measure in that it is accepted that every effort has been made to reduce the level of risk as far, as is possible. A principle, known as **'As low as reasonably practicable'**. Such a principle has been the basis of Health and Safety legislation enforcement in the United Kingdom for many years.

(iv) **Intolerable** – if the risk is not considered tolerable, then by definition, it becomes intolerable. Such risks cannot be tolerated under any circumstances.

3.4.8   For fire safety in buildings, the legislation applied in the United Kingdom is intended to provide a tolerable level of risk. The annual fire statistics provide a measure of this level of risk.

3.4.9   It is on this basis that any evaluation of a proposal that is seen as a departure from the more usual approval procedures, must be on the premise that the design will provide the same (or even lower) level of risk as would an equivalent, standard building. The present system of on-going control in respect of fire safety in occupied buildings required an ongoing evaluation of the circumstances by those responsible for enforcement – usually the fire brigade, in respect of the 'fire certificate' issued under the 1971 Fire Precautions Act. Under the Workplace Regulations (as amended), the fire brigade will enforce, but the assessment of the fire risk will be completed by the employer/responsible person.

Chapter 4 – Smoke control systems

4.1 Types of smoke control

4.1.1 Smoke control is usually by a system designed specifically for the building. This may be either:

(i)   A smoke and heat exhaust ventilation system (SHEVS);
(ii)   A pressure differential system.

In some circumstances where the fire load is low in a very high compartment the large roof void is used as an unventilated reservoir.

4.2 Smoke and heat exhaust ventilation systems (SHEVS)

4.2.1 Smoke control using smoke and heat exhaust ventilation systems (SHEVS) is designed to provide a smoke and heat free layer above an escape route by removing the smoke and heat generated by a fire, so creating conditions for safe escape or access for fire-fighting. SHEVS are expressly tailored for the building to which they are being applied from mathematical formulae developed specifically for that purpose.

4.2.2 There are two main types of SHEVS. They are:

(i)   Natural ventilation;
(ii)   Powered ventilation.

Natural ventilation systems rely on the natural buoyancy of hot smoke and gases to rise and escape to atmosphere through automatic ventilators situated in the roof of a building. Powered ventilation uses temperature rated fans, which start automatically to draw hot smoke and gases from the upper parts of the building.

4.2.3 Without replacement air, the ventilation system would not operate efficiently. The hot smoke removed either by natural or powered systems is replaced by air entering through low level inlets which automatically open when the system is activated. Normal entrance doors are often used for this purpose. In natural ventilation systems, fans sometimes supply replacement air. Total powered systems, sometimes referred to as "push–pull systems", where both the inlet air and smoke exhaust are fan assisted are rarely used.

4.2.4 Powered ventilation systems generally have a fixed rate or capacity of exhaust, although that can be influenced by the factors listed below. The capacity of natural ventilation systems depends on a number of factors, including:

(i)   The temperature of the smoke laden gas.
(ii)   The aero-dynamic free area of the ventilators.
(iii)   The size of the inlet air openings.
(iv)   Wind influence.

4.2.5 SHEVS are often arranged in zones. Each zone is separated from the other by walls and/or smoke barriers and has its own smoke control system, powered or natural. Adjacent zones having powered systems may use a common extraction fan through inter-connecting ducts. However, each zone should have its own replacement air inlet arrangements. The system is triggered by a smoke detection system in each zone. Where zones share a common extract fan, smoke control dampers in the common duct operate to ensure that only the fire zone is connected to the extract fan and that all other openings are closed.

4.2.6 SHEVS will operate when buoyant smoke from a fire in a ventilated zone rises into a smoke reservoir and triggers a smoke detection system. This will either cause the exhaust vents to open or start the exhaust fans in a powered system. At the same time, the replacement air inlets will open so creating airflow in the protected area. The smoke reservoir will fill at the calculated rate until the fire is suppressed by fire-fighting tactics, e.g. sprinklers, and maintains the fire size and controls the maximum temperature of the smoke to within design limits.

4.3   Application of SHEVS to buildings

4.3.1 In buildings such as shopping complexes, the malls and other common areas which make up the main public concourses would be the means which the public would use for escape in the event of a fire in an adjoining shop. It follows, therefore, that these areas must be kept as smoke-free for as long as possible in such an event.

4.3.2 In a fire the hot smoky gases will pass out of the shop front and rise to the mall ceiling mixing with fresh air as they go. Without smoke control measures, hot smoke and gases will flow along a mall, at a speed typically between 1 and 2 metres per second. This is probably faster than the escape speed of pedestrians in a crowded mall.

4.3.3 SHEVS should be designed to control the smoke layer to a maximum depth below ceiling level by venting the hot smoke and gases to open air and before they cool and fall to contaminate the upper walkways of the mall. The design should also take into account the possibility of the rising smoke plume swirling back as it passes upper balconies or walkways being used by people escaping.

4.3.4 Rising hot smoke and gases are contained in a reservoir from which they are discharged to atmosphere. The reservoir can be either a permanent feature of the structure or be formed from moving screens or barriers being lowered when automatic fire detectors actuate the system.

4.4 Design of smoke reservoirs

4.4.1 Smoke reservoirs should form smoke zones. There may be more than one reservoir in any compartment but no reservoir should serve more than one compartment. Each reservoir should be large enough to retain the volume of smoke that will enter it in the design fire scenario.

4.4.2 The capacity of the ventilators serving reservoirs should be sufficient to retain the base height of smoke-laden gas at predicted levels within the range of likely smoke temperatures. Where reservoirs are not a permanent structural feature but are formed by moveable barriers or partitions being lowered at the time of a fire, details of those arrangements, their actuating mechanisms and, where appropriate power supplies should be taken into account. In life safety systems, movable equipment should fail in an effective operational condition.

4.4.3 A reservoir should not be more than 60m long so as to avoid people having to move below the smoke layer for extended periods, so causing them concern.

4.5 Removal of hot smokes and gases

4.5.1 Hot smoke and gases can be removed from the reservoirs either by natural or powered ventilation. The rate of exhaust must be approximately equal to the probable rate at which hot smoke and gases will enter the reservoir from a fully developed fire.

4.5.2 Fresh air must enter the ventilated area at a rate at least equal to the rate of extraction and low enough not to prematurely mix with and thus cool the hot smoke and gases. The siting of the exit points where the hot smoke and gases leave the building also needs consideration to avoid creating a hazard elsewhere.

4.5.3 Where there is likelihood that external wind forces on sloping roofs of more than 30° will adversely affect natural ventilation, either windshields should be provided to protect the ventilator; or additional ventilators provided which are under the control of a wind sensor. Sufficient of the additional ventilators should be available at any one time to meet the needs of the system. Alternatively, powered ventilators should be provided.

4.6 Smoke controls using pressurisation

4.6.1 An alternative form of smoke control may be by means of pressure differential system. Here the air pressure in the means of escape route is increased sufficiently to prevent smoke from a fire in an adjacent area from entering the area. Because of the difficulty of pressurising a large area sufficiently quickly to prevent the ingress of smoke, a pressure differential system is normally limited to smaller areas.

4.6.2 The most common use of pressurisation is in escape stairways, particularly where a lack of natural ventilation creates a risk of smoke logging. Pressurisation may also be used in conjunction with smoke ventilation in atria buildings. Here, the atria are ventilated by a SHEVS or similar system whilst adjacent areas other than the fire area are de-pressurised to prevent the ingress of smoke and heat.

4.6.3 Pressurisation provides a pressure differential between the fire area and essential escape routes and fire-fighting access routes to keep them clear of smoke for extended periods. Pressurisation systems inject air into the protected escape routes i.e. staircases, lobbies or corridors, which raises the pressure slightly above that of adjacent parts of the building. This prevents smoke and toxic gases from entering the protected routes.

4.6.4 To be effective in accordance with British Standard BS 5588: Part 4, a smoke control system using pressure differentials must achieve a higher pressure than those developed by weather and fire conditions. The recommended level of pressurisation is about 45–50Pa (Pascal) with all doors closed. This represents approximately ten times the pressure normally developed in a fire and is about four times the maximum pressure likely to be caused by adverse weather conditions. The airflow required to achieve this pressure is independent of the volume of space to be pressurised. In deciding on the airflow required it is necessary to take the leakage paths into account.

4.6.5 The pressurised area must be provided with adequate leakage paths, to ensure that the necessary pressure differential between the fire area and the protected zone can be maintained.

4.6.6 In most cases the leakage path will be past gaps around doors and windows from non-pressurised accommodation space or through lift doors. Usually the doors enclosing a pressurised space will also need to be fire resistant, which should ensure a door that is close-fitting to the frame.

4.6.7 Where windows or doors do not provide sufficient leakage or where more precise leakage path is required, dedicated vents may be provided arranged to open when the pressurisation system is actuated.

4.6.8 In a fire situation, people will have to open doors in the pressurised area as they escape from the building. The momentary opening of doors should not seriously affect the pressurisation system and any pressure loss should be quickly recovered when the doors close again. Where people escaping are using the protected route or for fire-fighting access, it is likely that doors, especially the final exit door, will be open continuously. In these circumstances the pressurisation system in accordance with British Standard BS 5588: Part 4 should be capable of maintaining a pressure of not less than 10Pa.

4.6.9 A pressure of 50Pa will mean that a little extra pressure will be required to open a door leading to the pressurised area. This is sufficiently small to allow most people to open such doors and in all cases should not exceed 100N (Newtons).

Chapter 5 – Suppression, Detection and Compartmentation

5.1   Sprinklers

5.1.1   Except in smaller applications of fire safety engineering, some form of automatic suppression system(s) may be necessary to keep the fire within the designed limits of the engineering employed. Whilst eventual fire service intervention will limit the maximum fire size, in life safety schemes that intervention should not be relied on as the sole means of fire suppression.

5.1.2   In most cases where buildings are protected by smoke and heat exhaust ventilation systems, sprinklers are usually installed to restrict the growth potential of a fire to its design size. Larger fires may produce excessive amounts of hot smoke contaminated gases sufficient to overwhelm the ventilation system.

5.1.3   Sprinkler systems should be designed in accordance with BS 5306-2 or BS EN 12259 to a category that meets the fire load conditions likely to be found in the relevant parts of the building. Those categories are:

(i) Light hazard

  (a)   Ordinary hazard: Group I
  (b)   Ordinary hazard: Group II
  (c)   Ordinary hazard: Group III
  (d)   Ordinary hazard: Group III Special

(ii) High hazard

Further details of the hazard ratings can be found in the Technical Standards.

5.1.4   Sprinklers should be installed in any part of the building where the potential fire development is likely to put people escaping at risk. Where the efficiency of the ventilation system relies on the buoyancy of hot smoke, care should be taken to ensure that the cooling effect of sprinklers, where they are also provided, does not compromise that efficiency below acceptable levels.

5.1.5   The effects of sprinkler discharge close to natural ventilators can also compromise the efficiency of the ventilator.

5.1.6   Where the ventilation system and sprinkler system are provided for property protection only and not life protection, it is sometimes considered advantageous to allow the sprinkler system to operate automatically but to restrict ventilation until the fire service attends and can activate the ventilation manually.

5.1.7   The system may include flow switches arranged to activate the ventilation equipment and other facilities upon detection of a fire.

5.2   Automatic fire detection and fire warning systems

5.2.1   The smoke control systems in buildings are best activated by an automatic fire detection system installed in areas where the smoke control system is effective. These may be either in the area where the fire is likely to occur or in the area from which smoke is to be vented. The type of detection should be chosen carefully not only to ensure the smoke control system operates when needed but also to minimise false alarms.

5.2.2   Ambient air temperatures at ceiling level in heated buildings or those subject to solar gain may form a high level plug of air which is hotter than the temperature of smoke and gases from a fire in its initial stages. The hot plug will cause the smoke to stratify at a point where the temperature of the smoke and that of the lower part of the hot plug are roughly the same. If the smoke detectors are set at ceiling level, the smoke will not reach them and thus the smoke control system will not operate. To avoid this, the smoke detectors should be set at a lower level, below the point where stratification is likely. Often beam type detectors provide a better solution to this problem than point detectors.

5.2.3   The fire warning system may be divided into zones. These zones should be co-terminus with the smoke control zones so that no fire-warning zone extends beyond a smoke control zone. This will ensure that at the time of a fire, only the smoke control system in the fire zone will be operated. The operation of systems in adjacent smoke zones could adversely affect the efficiency of the equipment in the fire zone.

5.2.4   The building may use two stage, phased or progressive horizontal evacuation according to that deemed most appropriate for its use. The fire warning system may be used to control the sequencing of people escaping. The initial fire evacuation signal need not necessarily be tied into the configuration of smoke zones but must include the fire zone.

5.2.5   Most buildings will require a fire warning system, which is capable of being operated manually by persons discovering a fire using break glass call points.

5.2.6   The possibility of persons escaping operating a manual fire alarm call point in a smoke zone that is remote from the fire zone should be identified. Such operation could activate the smoke control system in a smoke zone, which is not the fire zone. This could reduce the efficiency of the smoke control in the fire zone, particularly where shared ducted systems with damper selection are used. It may be advisable to link manual call points into the fire alarm system to give an initial alert signal and in a manner where they will not activate the smoke control systems. This would ensure that when the automatic detection in the fire zone operates, the evacuation signal and the correct operation of the smoke control systems will be assured.

5.3 Compartmentation

5.3.1 To augment the fire engineering provided in the building, compartmentation may be necessary to:

(i)   Restrict travel distances to acceptable lengths.
(ii)   Support the evacuation strategy selected for the building.
(iii)   Restrict fire growth to within designed limits.
(iv)   Separate areas protected by fire engineering from unprotected areas.

5.3.2 The maximum size of compartments and the levels of fire resistance necessary to ensure the integrity of the structure during a fire will depend on a number of factors. These are given in Approved Document 'B' and these include:

(i)   Ceiling height of compartment.
(ii)   Depth below building access level.
(iii)   Height above building access level.
(iv)   Use of building and occupant risk category.
(v)   Sprinklers or other suitable automatic suppression.
(vi)   Ventilation factor (non-engineered).
(vii)   Fire load.

5.3.3 The fire resistance and extent of compartmentation may be varied because of the engineering employed. However, care should be taken to ensure that over large compartments do not put the structure at risk. Furthermore, the effect of a fire in the proposed building on adjacent buildings must also be taken into account.

5.4 Automatic systems

5.4.1 Automatic systems in this context means equipment within the building aimed at maintaining compartmentation. These include:

(i)   Shutters.
(ii)   Self-closing doors.
(iii)   Dampers.
(iv)   Fire door and shutter hold open devices.

The effect of environmental ventilation ducting and fans on compartmentation should also be taken into account.

Chapter 6 – Means of escape in case of fire

6.1 General

6.1.1 The means of escape from buildings where fire safety engineering has been installed to maintain safe exit routes should follow the same principles as that used in buildings using passive fire safety. The main difference between the two techniques is that, in the fire engineered building, the travel distances may be longer and the fire resisting protection to escape routes may be to lower ratings. However, the standards of safety achieved should be at least equivalent to those that could be achieved using existing fire safety measures.

6.1.2 The implied standards in passive standards need to be positively addressed. In particular the probable behaviour and the characteristics of people in the building, at the time of a fire need to be carefully considered.

6.1.3 The means of escape philosophy in the fire engineered building are based on time related factors. Realistic times should be used, where possible based on research carried out in buildings of similar design or use.

6.1.4 The time envisaged for a person to reach a place of safety or relative safety should be measured from the time the evacuation alarm signal is given. This must always be within the time available for escape, measured from the time the fire is first detected.

6.2 Calculating escape times

6.2.1 When calculating the time for escape, the following factors should be taken into account:

(i) Occupant characteristics;
(ii) Hazard assessment and probable fire growth rate;
(iii) The evacuation strategy of the building;
(iv) The probable time between ignition and alarm;
(v) Average movement speed of people along designated escape routes;
(vi) Probable total time of escape;
(vii) Probable total time where a person may be particularly at risk;
(viii) Psychological effects on escapees particularly those who may have sight of fire or its effects;
(ix) Management input into evacuation process.

6.3   Occupant characteristics

6.3.1   Occupant characteristic should identify the class of person who might be in the building and what they may be doing at the time of a fire, thus they should consider:

(i)   Occupants' familiarity with the building.

(ii)   Occupant commitment at the time of alarm.

(iii)   Occupant commitment after alarm but before commencing escape, e.g. helping others, fire-fighting etc.

(iv)   Physical effort required to use escape routes e.g. stairs, upward escape routes.

(v)   Psychological effects on escapees particularly those who may have sight of fire or its effects or who may have to wait before commencing their escape.

(vi)   The physical capabilities of the occupants, i.e. wheelchair users or others with physical disabilities or compromised hearing and sight.

6.4   Hazard Assessment

6.4.1   A hazard assessment will have been carried out to determine the extent and viability of the fire engineering installed. This should also identify where fires are more probable or where rapid-fire growth rates might be expected. The hazard assessment should also identify sources of heat, particularly those in contact with combustible materials.

6.5   Evacuation Strategy

6.5.1   The evacuation strategy for the building will depend on its use, size and height; the characteristics of the occupants and the degree of fire resisting compartmentation, as agreed with the enforcing authorities.

6.5.2   The evacuation strategy for the building will determine:

(i)   The capacity of escape routes.

(ii)   The configuration and type of the fire alarm system.

(iii)   The configuration of the smoke control system.

(iv) . The compartmentation of the building.

(v)   The management requirements for the building.

(vi)   Time between ignition and alarm.

6.6   Time between ignition and alarm

6.6.1   The probable time between ignition and alarm will depend on the type of detection employed. No building provided with engineered fire safety should rely only on discovery of fire by people. All should be fitted with some form of reliable automatic detection system programmed to keep unwanted calls to a minimum.

6.6.2   Detection should be at the point first involved in fire, thus ensuring that an early alarm of fire is given. The signal from the first point of detection need not activate the smoke control or other active systems but may prime those systems where 'double knock' detection is used for activation.

6.7   Probable time for escape

6.7.1   The probable time for escape will depend on the distance a person may have to travel and the speed of travel. This may be dependant on the physical capabilities of those concerned, i.e. those wheelchair users or those with other permanent or temporary physical disabilities and those with family dependencies.

6.7.2   Generally the greater the number of persons the slower they will move. It should be ensured that the likely numbers of persons occupying any part of the building at the same time is in accordance with accepted density tables.

6.7.3   People will move faster on flat surfaces but will slow for steps, stair or ramps.

6.7.4   The widths of escape routes should be sufficient to accommodate the numbers of persons likely to use them. Account should be taken of additional numbers of people who may use an exit as an alternative escape route if their primary route is unavailable.

6.7.5   The effects of probable queuing where the movement of people will normally slow should be acknowledged. Slowing will also occur where people have to pass through doors, negotiate stairs or where they merge with people escaping from another part of the building.

6.8   People at particular risk

6.8.1   People will be particularly at risk from fire, heat or smoke when:

(i)   They are within the enclosure in which the fire first starts;
(ii)   They are passing under smoke flowing towards or held in a smoke reservoir;
(iii)   They are at a higher level and thus closer to smoke held in a smoke reservoir;
(iv)   Their primary escape route is blocked causing them to travel a longer distance to a suitable, alternative exit;
(v)   They are required to carry out specific duties such as helping others or carry out fire-fighting duties before they can themselves escape.

6.8.2   The time required for these people to escape may be longer or the time available for escape shorter than in normal circumstances. The design should demonstrate that sufficient time is available for people who may be particularly at risk, to escape safely.

6.9 Psychological effects

6.9.1 Ideally, the engineering design should provide for people to escape to safety, without coming into contact with a fire or its effects. However, there may be circumstances where people may have to move in smoke or in an area where they will be aware of a fire. The design should take account of the reluctance of some people to move into areas where they perceive danger. This may be by ensuring that their movement in smoke is minimal with low concentrations of smoke being assured. Keeping the time people may have sight of the fire to a minimum is essential as is ensuring those confronted with fire or its effects can see an exit sign. Staff should be designated to assist those with disabilities or other occupants who will require assistance. They should also assist people who may be unfamiliar with the building.

6.9.2 Some people may leave an area of immediate danger, but then pause to view the fire, thus putting themselves at risk and hindering those who are in the earlier stages of evacuation. The rate of evacuation should be maintained by frequent broadcast messages urging people to leave the building and by staff intervention at the points where the evacuation impetus slows.

6.9.3 Exit routes should be indicated and well lit, care being taken to ensure that an adequate lighting level is maintained in circumstances where natural light and artificial light are obscured by smoke. Care should be taken to ensure that where extended evacuation times are envisaged that firefighters entering the building do not hinder the escape process. Persons who have evacuated the building should be assembled in a place where they can congregate safely, away from any falling debris from the building and from the fire-fighting operation.

6.9.4 Trained staff or others should be at hand to assist people who are traumatised or suffering physical distress.

6.10 Evacuation of people with disabilities

6.10.1 Decision making in this area of fire safety would be determined by the guidance given in British Standard BS 5588: Part 8 – Fire Precautions in the design and construction of buildings – Code of Practice for means of escape for disabled people.

6.10.2 One significant aspect of means of escape provisions for people with disabilities may depend on the provision of refuges, i.e. places of relative safety where people may wait for assistance in making their escape.

6.10.3 Refuges are relative safe waiting areas for short periods only. They are not areas where people with disabilities should be left alone indefinitely until they are rescued by the fire brigade, or until the fire is extinguished.

6.10.4   Therefore, a robust management system should be in place in line with the guidance given in the British Standard. Additional information in the form of contact address in Annex B of the British Standard is available where further guidance could be obtained.

6.10.5   This provision is reinforced by the impact of the Fire Precautions (Workplace) Regulations, as amended. Within these Regulations (the Fire Regulations) is a primary responsibility on the employer to ensure the safety of employees from the effect of fire.

6.10.6   The Fire Regulations, together with the Management of Health and Safety at Work Regulations 1999 (MHSWR), are both based on risk assessment of the building and as such are fluid with changing circumstances so that the level of detail in the risk assessment should remain proportionate to the risk in question.

6.10.7   There is also general guidance in Part 3 on the supporting guidance document issued to support the Fire Precautions (Workplace) Regulations, as amended. This is titled 'Fire Safety – An Employers Guide. There is specific guidance in this section relating to people with disabilities and means of escape in case of fire.

6.10.8   Consideration also needs to be given to the issue of manual handling and this should be considered in the overall risk assessment under the MHSWR.

6.10.9   These suggestions will not obviously reduce the need for appropriate training of sufficient staff to carry out specific duties in a fire emergency situation. The training, roles and responsibilities should be robust and incorporated into the risk assessment that would apply to situations during the normal day time and hours outside this period, if applicable.

Chapter 7 – Management and Fire-fighting

7.1 Management

7.1.1 The management plan should include specific requirements for designated staff to oversee the evacuation process at the time of a fire. This will include directing the evacuation sequence, where phased evacuation is employed.

7.1.2 Designated staff should receive adequate training and have knowledge of the designed function of the fire safety engineering systems installed in the building. Good communications between the person in ultimate charge and other, designated staff is essential.

7.2 First aid fire-fighting

7.2.1 To comply with fire safety legislation it will normally be necessary for the design to include first aid fire-fighting equipment. This may be by hand held appliances as appropriate to the risk.

7.2.2 Fire-fighting equipment for use by properly trained staff can reduce the risk to other persons from that fire. A small fire tackled in its early stages of development may prevent it from developing into life threatening proportions, particularly if the initial fire involves substances where water is not a suitable extinguishing medium.

7.2.3 Whilst there may be some slight additional risk to staff engaged in fire-fighting, rather than them leaving the building immediately the fire is discovered and the alarm actuated, the benefit to others in extinguishing a small fire outweighs that risk. Claims that the provision of fire-fighting equipment and the training to staff to use that equipment imposes too great a risk to those engaged in fire-fighting should be viewed with caution.

7.2.4 The provision of first aid fire-fighting equipment and its probable effects on fire growth rates should not be taken into account when determining the design fire size.

7.3 Fire service facilities

7.3.1 To comply with building control legislation, the design should include access arrangements for the fire service. These arrangements should be in accordance with current advice on fire-fighting access.

7.3.2   When planning access routes, the points where the evacuation of occupants may hinder access by firefighters should be identified. The location of control rooms, sprinkler stop valves and facilities to operate or adjust the smoke control systems, as appropriate, should be agreed with the fire service at the design stage.

7.3.3   A fire control room will probably be necessary in all large complexes, particularly those using phased evacuation. The fire control room should be readily accessible, preferably from open air and from the point where fire fighters will arrive, when summoned. All information regarding the precise location of a fire and status of fire detection, sprinkler and smoke control systems should be available in the control room.

7.3.4   Adequate water supplies should be provided and easily accessible by firefighters from any point of access into the building. Where appropriate this may include the provision of dry or wet mains within the building. Ideally, the initial access point for firefighters should not be on a major escape route from the building.

7.3.5   Where necessary, access within the building should include protected fire-fighting shafts and fire lifts.

7.3.6   Where a design takes into account the effect of firefighter intervention in determining a fire scenario, the designer should take into account the probable attendance time of appliances from the nearest fire station and the probable time from arrival to the application of the first fire-fighting jet. Cognisance should also be taken of occasions where the first attendance may be delayed.

7.3.7   However, the design strategy should not be dependant on fire service arrival and attack.

7.3.8   Where effective fire-fighting necessary to maintain a fire within its designed parameters involves resources beyond the scope of the first attendance, the probable attendance times of distant appliances and the actual time that a full fire-fighting commitment can be achieved should be reflected in the fire growth predictions.

Chapter 8 – Fire safety enforcement

8.1 General

8.1.1 Buildings employing fire safety engineering are often large and complex. This can often place a burden on enforcement authorities who must satisfy themselves that the total design is viable and will provide an acceptable level of safety. However, the assessment process can be shortened if certain key information is provided with the application.

8.1.2 In order that the correct information is provided, a checklist (see Chapter 9) should be used. This should be completed by the applicant and submitted as part of the building control approval application. The checklist can be useful to the designer in ensuring that the essential engineering criteria have been met and to the enforcer who will, therefore, be provided with a better understanding of the proposal without having to work through the mathematics supporting it.

8.1.3 The checklist should be divided into a series of questions, where the applicant can give the following key information regarding the fire engineering and other matters. This will include:

(i) General overview of scheme;
(ii) Hazard assessment, predicted fire size/rate of heat release;
(iii) Type and capacity of smoke control proposed;
(iv) Fire suppression;
(v) Predicted number and characteristics of people in building;
(vi) Means of escape and fire warning;
(vii) Fire-fighting access.

8.2 General overview of scheme

8.2.1 The applicant should give a brief summary of the building including its basic dimensions and its proposed use. The summary may include the relevant findings of the qualitative design review. This should include areas protected by fire engineering and the reasoning behind adopting a fire safety engineered design. The objectives of the engineering and a synopsis of the type and configuration of the engineering should be given.

8.2.2 An adequate maintenance and testing regime must support fire engineering. Enforcers should be satisfied that prospective occupants will have the necessary management skills to understand the purpose of the fire engineering and be able to ensure its reliability at all times. Bearing in mind that this will be for the projected life of the building. It must also recognise and accommodate that the use to which the building is put may change several times during its projected life. Any subsequent alterations to the building must not be allowed to compromise the original, approved, fire safety engineering scheme

8.2.3 The engineering used should be to a recognised design e.g. British Standard 7346 and be sufficiently robust to operate efficiently in the fire scenarios envisaged for the building.

8.3 Hazard assessment and design fire

8.3.1 The development of a fire to a steady state condition and its maximum heat release will depend on a number of factors, including:

(i) The nature, quantity and flammability of the materials present.

(ii) Air access to the fire through the configuration of the materials relative to themselves (i.e. wooden pallets with large air gaps) or the shielding effects of walls and ceilings relative to the materials etc.

(iii) The availability of air.

(iv) The effectiveness of sprinklers or other suppression devices.

8.3.2 Whilst a detailed hazard assessment may not be available at the design stage, the designer should give details of the assessment made and of the likely fire spread potential of materials to be used or stored in the completed building, by compartment. In particular, materials likely to promote rapid-fire spread, either because of their nature or the manner in which they are stored or used, should be identified.

8.3.3 The location of sources of heat and places in the building where the probability of fire is higher should be identified.

8.3.4 The classification of all materials should be given using Table 7.1 "Fuel Density Bands" in the Code of Practice BS5588 for fire safety in the design, construction and use of buildings. Predicted fire growth rates should be given using Table 4.3.2. "Fire Growth Rates" in the Code of Practice.

8.3.5 The calculated maximum temperature of the fire should be given by the designer, together with the calculated heat release rate. The designer will need to demonstrate how this was determined. Predicted fire sizes should be compatible with the hazard assessment. The applicant should demonstrate how the fire temperature and fire size is to be restricted within predictions and the fire configuration envisaged. This may be by compartmenting the structure or by automatic suppression or both.

8.3.6 The calculation of heat release values from fires often cannot be accurately predicted due to the range of materials that might be involved. The designer should agree a suitable fire scenario with the enforcing authorities at an early stage of the design.

8.3.7   For the purposes of calculating outputs from fires, the following values in different uses of premises are suitable for the normal fuel sources below 4m in height in the class of premises quoted.

Occupancy	Fire Area m²	Fire perimeter m	Heat release kWm²
Retail			
A	10	12	625
B	5	9	625
C	Entire room	Width of opening	1200
Offices			
A	16	14	225
C*	47	24	255
Hotel bedroom			
A	2	6	250
C	Entire room	Width of opening	255

A = Standard response sprinkler
B = Quick response sprinklers
C = No sprinklers
C* = No Sprinklers – fuel bed controlled.

NB:
(i)   Heat release is the heat energy released per unit of time from burning materials under normal fire conditions.
(ii)   Width of opening is the perimeter of heat release through an opening in a confined space (e.g. door of a room).

8.3.8   In cases where the occupancy is not listed above, the height of the fuel source should be given. Where this is given as higher than 4m, sprinklers would normally be expected to be included in the design. Where the fuel height is lower than 4m, the likely area and perimeter of the fuel source should be based on the probable physical extent of the fuel. Where there is a mix of fuel sources, the worst case scenario, i.e. a fire involving the more hazardous materials, should be applied. Where the percentage of high hazard materials is low, the average effect should be assumed.

8.3.9   Generally, the heat output of sprinkler controlled fires can be assumed to be in the order of between 1 and 5MW (see conductive heat flux below). Sprinklers would normally be expected to control a fire situation before this upper limit was reached. Enforcers should not accept life safety schemes without automatic suppression based on average fire sizes or where fire service intervention is the only means of fire control.

8.4 Smoke control

8.4.1 The designer should state the type of smoke control proposed and the location it is protecting.

8.5 Pressurisation

8.5.1 The location and capacity of fans on pressurisation systems conforming to British Standard BS 5588: Part 4, should either be given and/or shown on plan. Air drawn in by fans should be from open air. Care should be taken with the siting of fans that air drawn in, cannot be contaminated by smoke exiting from the fire. Where flaps or grills protect intakes, it should be ensured that these would open and be free from obstruction in all weather conditions.

8.5.2 The fans should be capable of achieving a pressure in the range of 45–50Pa with all doors closed. A minimum pressure of 10Pa should be achievable with one door fully open for extended periods.

8.5.3 The time interval between the activation of the pressurisation equipment and full pressure being achieved should be given.

8.5.4 The description of pressurisation systems should include arrangements for controlled leakage, showing the location of dedicated vents, where these are fitted. The power supplies for fans should be described.

8.5.5 Pressurisation systems are generally not suitable for large areas due to the probable delay before the system can generate sufficient pressure to be effective. They are best suited to protected stairway shafts or smaller atria applications where the volume to be pressurised is relatively small and confined.

8.5.6 Where pressurisation is installed for life safety purposes, dual power supplies must be specified.

8.6 Smoke and heat exhaust ventilation systems (SHEVS)

8.6.1 Smoke and heat exhaust ventilation systems are suitable for many types of building and are most frequently found in warehouses, enclosed shopping malls and large atria. The design, configuration and capacity of SHEVS will have been calculated mathematically. The formula for calculating SHEVS requirements are complex but applicants should provide the necessary information to demonstrate the viability of a proposal.

8.6.2 SHEVS are designed around a "design fire". In life safety applications, SHEVS should maintain a clear air layer above escape routes high enough for people to use them without breathing smoke contaminated air. The temperature of the gases in the buoyant layer under which people may have to pass should not exceed 200°C. The recommended minimum height of clear air is:

Type of building	Minimum height
Public buildings (e.g. single storey malls, exhibition halls)	3m
Non public buildings (e.g. offices, apartments, prisons)	2.5m
Car parks	2.5m or 0.8 of floor height (whichever is smaller)

NB:

Where the temperature of the hot smoke and gases is likely to be less than 50°C above ambient temperature, the heights quoted above must be increased by 0.5m.

8.6.3   The designer should state whether the SHEVS will be either by natural ventilation or powered ventilation. All SHEVS must have an adequate supply of replacement air to be effective. The entry points for replacement air should be specified or shown on plan. Inlet air should always enter the building at low level, below the smoke layer.

8.6.4   Where the replacement air is admitted through doors or passages used for means of escape purposes, the air speeds when the system is operating to capacity should not exceed 5m/sec. Nor should a pressure greater than 100N be necessary on the door handle to open a door into the air-stream (less in the case of elderly persons or children using the door). Doors used as air inlets should open automatically when the system is activated, even when the premises are closed and the door is locked against intruders.

8.6.5   Smoke and heat exhaust ventilation systems are not suitable where the predicted height from the base of the fire (usually the floor) to the base of the smoke layer in a reservoir is less than 10% of the height from the floor to the ceiling.

8.6.6   Smoke and heat exhaust ventilation systems are not suitable where the height from the base of the fire (the floor) to the base of the smoke layer is more than 90% of the height from the base of the fire to the ceiling.

8.7   Smoke reservoirs

8.7.1   The SHEVS design should provide for smoke and hot gases from a fire to rise by natural buoyancy into a smoke reservoir. From there ventilators will exhaust the smoke and gas to open air.

8.7.2   The designer should provide the calculated mass flow rate and the temperature of hot smoke and gases from a design fire collecting in a reservoir. The design temperature of smoke-laden gases entering a smoke reservoir should be assumed as .8 of the heat release rate of the design fire. At no time should the design temperature be less than 20°C above ambient temperature. The calculations should also reflect the cooling effect of sprinklers.

8.7.3   The mass flow rate will be determined by the conductive heat flux generated by the fire. A typical conductive heat flux flowing from a fire is:

Room description	Convective heat flux (MW)
Shop – sprinklered	5
Shop – fast response sprinkler	2.5
Office sprinklered	1
Office unsprinklered	6
Hotel bedroom unsprinklered	1

NB

Except for cases in which the designer can prove otherwise, for example:

(i)   For all other unsprinklered occupancies, the conductive heat flux should be taken as 0.5 times the calculated heat release rate of the design fire, or

(ii)   In the case of other sprinklered occupancies the convective heat flux should be taken as 0.25 times the calculated heat release rate of the design fire.

(iii)   If gases leaving a room are calculated as being higher than 550°C, flashover may occur. In those circumstances, all of the contents of a room should be assumed to be involved in fire rendering the design fire calculations invalid.

8.7.4   Smoke barriers or other features forming smoke reservoirs should be at least 0.1m deeper than the calculated depth of the smoke layer. The area of smoke reservoirs should be restricted to:

Fire in area under reservoir		Fire in area adjacent to reservoir	
Powered vents	Natural vents	Powered vents	Natural vents
2600m^2	2000m^2	1300m^2	1000m^2

8.7.5   Where escape routes pass under a smoke reservoir, the maximum dimension in any direction should not exceed 60m.

8.7.6   Ventilators should be evenly distributed throughout a smoke reservoir with no part of the reservoir more than three times the width of the reservoir from a ventilator, unless a transfer duct is fitted.

8.7.7   The total capacity of powered ventilators or the total area of natural ventilators should be sufficient to exhaust the calculated mass flow entering the reservoir. In the case of natural ventilators, the designer should include arrangements to offset any adverse wind effects, which could reduce the efficiency of the system.

8.7.8   In the case of powered ventilators, over provision should be avoided for fear of drawing cold air through the hot gases causing premature cooling. In the case of natural ventilators where the cooling effect of sprinklers may have an adverse effect on their capacity, one ventilator should be discounted, the remainder being sufficient for the identified need.

8.8   Detection and activation

8.8.1   The ventilation system should be activated automatically by smoke or other suitable fire detection devices. The detection systems should be configured to ensure that only the appropriate smoke zone would be activated.

8.8.2   To avoid the situation where smoke may not reach the detectors because of hot air forming a plug in a smoke reservoir, the detectors should be located in positions where they can respond to smoke regardless of the ambient temperature in the reservoir.

8.8.3   To ensure early operation, the ventilation system should be linked into the general automatic fire warning system. To avoid the incorrect activation of the ventilation system, it should not respond to the activation of manual call points.

8.8.4   The fire warning system and fire detection systems should comply with British Standard 5839 and BS EN 54, as appropriate.

8.9   Compartmentation

8.9.1   Where compartments are necessary, their size and fire resisting separation should be in accordance with the appropriate table of Approved Document 'B' to the Building Regulations or any appropriate equivalent standard.

8.10   Means of escape

8.10.1   The classification of occupants who may use the building should be in accordance with Approved Document 'B' or British Standard BS 7974.

8.10.2   The means of escape from parts of the building protected by passive fire safety standards should be in accordance with the appropriate parts of Clause 6 of the proposed British Standard BS 9999 or any appropriate equivalent standard.

8.10.3   The means of escape form those parts of the building protected by fire safety engineering (protected area) should be within the design parameters of the engineering and ensure that:

(i)   Every part of the protected area has realistic alternative escape routes.

(ii)   Any person entering a protected area should be able to find their way to safety without the assistance of other persons.

(iii)   No persons should be required to move in smoke for more than 15 seconds.

(iv)   No person should be required to move under smoke for more than 3 minutes.

(v)   The maximum time a person should be in the same part of the building as the fire, other than in a protected route, should not exceed 7 minutes.

8.10.4 Occupational densities should be calculated using Approved Document 'B' to the Building Regulations or other appropriate guidance.

8.10.5 The minimum widths of exit doors and routes should be in accordance with the appropriate tables in Approved Document 'B'.

8.11   Management

8.11.1 Good fire safety management is an essential part of the overall levels of fire safety in the completed building. The management levels for the building should reflect Level 1 of Table 9.1 of proposed British Standard BS 9999 (BS 5588: Part 12).

8.11.2 In order to reduce the national wastage due to fires, individuals, property owners and employers have a clear duty (Fire Precautions (Workplace) Regulations 1997, as amended) to manage or control the risk posed by fires to life.

8.11.3 The actions taken by the Government following the introduction of Directives from the European Commission for managing fire risk include the above Regulations as well as other legislation in the form of the Fire Precautions Act 1971.

8.11.4 Although most such regulation, legislative measures, codes and standards provide minimum levels of fire protection for different types of property, the property owners are encouraged to consider additional cost-effective measures to enhance this basic level.

8.12   Fire-fighting access

8.12.1 Fire-fighting access arrangements should be in accordance with Clause 8 of the proposed British Standard BS 9999, British Standard BS 7974, and British Standard BS 5588: Part 5, Approved Document 'B' to the Building Regulations or other approved standard.

Chapter 9 – Fire Safety Engineering checklist

9.1 Introduction

In order to assist those responsible for the enforcement of fire safety legislation and the formal statutory approval of schemes or proposals submitted for building control approval, use of the following checklist is recommended. This checklist, which could accompany the application, will give those responsible for enforcement or approval, ready access to key information, which can be compared with values quoted in other sections of this Manual.

This will enable those responsible for enforcement or approval to make a realistic assessment of the application and it's engineering without necessarily having to validate the mathematics supporting the proposal in every case.

9.2 General overview of scheme

9.2.1 Description of building.

    (i)   Footprint area.
    (ii)   Number of floors.
    (iii)   Height of atrium or mall if appropriate.

9.2.2 Intended use(s) and location of use(s).

9.2.3 Fire safety-engineering objectives.

9.2.4 Life safety

    (i)   Property protection.

9.2.5 Principal type of engineering proposed.

    (i)   Exhaust ventilation.
    (ii)   Pressurisation.
    (iii)   Other (state).

9.2.6 Number and characteristics of people likely to use the building or any part thereof.

9.3   Hazard assessment

9.3.1   Nature, quantity and classification of fuel sources generally expected to be present.

9.3.2   Nature, quantity, classification and location of fuel sources likely to promote rapid fire spread.

9.3.3   Nature and location of heat sources likely to increase probability of fire.

9.4   Predicted/Design fire scenario

9.4.1   Fire perimeter in metres.

9.4.2   Calculated heat release in kWm^2.

9.4.3   Height of fuel source.

9.4.4   Fire area in m^2.

9.4.5   Means proposed to retain fire within design predictions.

9.4.6   Classification of fuel source used in calculation.

9.5   Conductive heat flux

9.5.1   The calculated conductive heat flux from the design fire used in the calculations must be given.

9.6   Smoke and Heat Exhaust Ventilation Systems

Where smoke and heat ventilation systems are proposed the following information should be given:

9.6.1   Type of system e.g. natural or powered.

9.6.2   Location in building of system(s).

9.6.3   Objective of system(s).

9.6.4   Number of smoke reservoirs proposed.

9.6.5   Probable fire under or adjacent to reservoir.

9.6.6   Area of reservoirs in m^2.

9.6.7   Maximum length of reservoir in any direction.

9.6.8   Minimum depth of reservoir.

9.6.9   Maximum depth of smoke layer in reservoir from design fire.

9.6.10   Maximum distance from the base of fire to base of smoke layer.

9.6.11   Maximum temperature of smoke in reservoir from design fire.

9.6.12   Minimum clear air space between base of smoke layer and floor of means of escape route.

9.6.13   Maximum ambient temperature of air in reservoir before fire.

9.6.14   Maximum distance from any part of a reservoir to a ventilator or ventilator duct.

9.6.15   Maximum temperature of base of smoke layer at minimum distance above means of escape route.

9.6.16   Calculated mass flow into reservoir from design fire.

9.6.17   Capacity of ventilators with smoke at maximum temperature.

9.6.18   Arrangements to counter adverse wind effects.

9.6.19   Arrangements to counter any adverse sprinkler effects.

9.6.20   Air inlet arrangements.

9.6.21   Where doorways are used, maximum air velocity likely on escape routes with system at maximum capacity.

9.6.22   Measured force on door openings on air inlet routes.

9.6.23   Pressure necessary on door handles or push plates by people using air inlet route as a means of escape route.

9.6.24   Means for activating system.

9.6.25   Arrangements for ensuring that detection equipment will sense fire or smoke in all environments within protected area and provide a feedback to the central control panel.

9.6.26   Power supplies for powered systems and detection equipment and the type of cable used.

9.7   Pressure Differential systems

Where pressurisation systems are proposed the following information should be given:

9.7.1   Areas to be pressurised and the class of system.

9.7.2   Capacity of fans used for pressurisation.

9.7.3   Design pressures achievable with all doors closed.

9.7.4   Design pressures achievable with one door continuously open.

9.7.5   Interval between system being actuated and design pressure being achieved.

9.7.6   Arrangements for allowing controlled leakage from pressurised area.

9.7.7   Means of activating system.

9.7.8   Power supplies for system and the type of cable used.

9.8   Atria

Where Atria are proposed the following information should be given:

9.8.1   Atria should be designed in accordance with BS 5588: Part 7.

9.8.2   Information on smoke exhaust ventilation systems should be given in accordance with Section 9.6 above

9.8.3   Information on pressurisation systems should be given in accordance with Section 9.7 above

9.9   Fire detection and alarm systems

Where fire detection and alarm systems are proposed the following information should be given:

9.9.1   The fire detection and alarm system should comply with the relevant parts of BS 5839 or BS EN 54.

9.9.2   Where the system is linked into the smoke control activating system, the means for ensuring that only the smoke control system in the fire area will be activated should be demonstrated.

9.9.3   Where staged or phased evacuation is proposed, details of the control position and, where appropriate, examples of verbal messages should given.

9.9.4   Type, location and audibility of fire alarm sounders should be given.

9.10   Sprinkler and fire-fighting systems

Sprinklers must be designed and installed to the relevant hazard criteria and be in accordance with BS EN 12259. Where sprinkler and fire-fighting systems are proposed the following information should be given:

9.10.1   The area(s) within the proposal where sprinklers will be installed should be indicated.

9.10.2   The category of sprinkler system proposed should be given together with details of intended water supplies.

9.10.3   Types of sprinkler heads (i.e. normal or quick response) should be given.

9.10.4   The location of sprinkler valve chambers and auxiliary controls should be indicated.

9.10.5   Details of equipment interfaced with or driven by the sprinkler installation should be given.

9.10.6   Details of the sprinkler installation should include the maintenance and testing schedules

9.10.7   Where special fixed fire-fighting equipment such as drenchers or foam generators are proposed, these should be included on the sprinkler schedule.

9.11   Means of escape in case of fire

9.11.1   The means of escape in case of fire from the non-engineered parts of the premises should also be shown on plan. The means of escape through the engineered parts of the building should also be shown on plan. The travel distance through the engineered parts or the calculated time for escape from those parts should be given. All routes should be signed as necessary.

9.11.2   The maximum time a person may have to travel below smoke or through the fire zone should be given. The total time between the evacuation signal being given and a person reaching a place of safety using the most direct route should be given. The total time between the evacuation signal being given and a person reaching a place of safety by the most direct alternative route should also be given.

9.11.3   Details of the proposed occupier management plan should be given. This should include:

(i)   Arrangements for evacuating the building;
(ii)   Staff training including the use of fire equipment;
(iii)   Maintenance schedules for the fire safety engineering equipment;
(iv)   Fire extinguisher testing;
(v)   Sprinkler testing.

This list is not exhaustive.

9.11.4   Levels of management should generally comply with management level one given in the draft British Standard, BS 9999 clause 9.

9.12   Fire-fighting access

9.12.1   Fire-fighting access arrangements and water supplies for fire-fighting should be agreed with the fire authority and comply with the recommendations given in the draft British Standard BS 9999 Clause 8, British Standard BS5588: Part 5 and Approved Document 'B' to the Building Regulations.

Chapter 10 – Standardisation of Fire Safety Engineering at National, European and International Levels

10.1 Introduction

10.1.1 As a result of the substantial increase in fire research during the last decades, many components and systems are becoming more amenable to analytical and computer modelling. Consequently many national building regulators, particularly in the United Kingdom have moved from a prescriptive approach to a performance-based approach. There is, therefore, a growing need to develop new technical standards to accommodate this trend. These will require a more cohesive approach to fire safety than has been possible in the past.

10.1.2 Concurrent with the work within the United Kingdom in British Standard Technical Committee FSH/24 – Fire Safety Engineering, work over several years within ISO TC92 – Fire Safety, Sub-committee 4 – Fire Safety Engineering, has led to the development of substantial documents covering the subject.

10.1.3 The ISO Technical Reports on fire safety engineering methodologies (TR 13387:Parts 1-8) were published in June 1999. Work on their refinement continues in the Sub-committee. The British Standards Institution published a Draft for Development (DD 240) which closely followed the principles of the ISO Technical Report. This Draft for Development has now been progressed to a full BS Code of Practice – BS 7974: 2001

10.1.4 This code of practice (BS 7974) provides a framework for developing a rational methodology for design of buildings using a fire safety engineering approach based on the application of scientific and engineering principles to the protection of people, property and the environment from fire.

10.1.5 For most buildings the supportive recommendations to the functional requirements of the Building Regulations on design in existing codes and guides, as given in BS 5588 – Fire Precautions in the design, construction and use of buildings: Part 0: Guide to fire safety codes of practice for particular premises/applications, may be found to be adequate. However, BS 7974 is intended to be used for developing and assessing fire safety-engineering proposals.

10.1.6   The Technical Reports (TR 13387: Parts 1–8), were prepared by the ISO Technical Committee ISO TC92 – Fire Safety: SC4 – Fire safety Engineering. These have been published by British Standards verbatim and, therefore implemented as a UK national standard and are available as an alternative reference.

10.1.7   The UK participation in their preparation was entrusted to BS Technical Committee FSH/24.

10.1.8   This series of ISO documents offers a slightly different approach to that in the British Standard BS 7974 and the Published Documents that accompany it. Given the present state of the art in relation to fire safety engineering at this time, neither approach can be regarded as the 'definitive' view.

10.1.9   As each separate approach offers an alternative and given the consideration now required of both the BS Published Documents and the ISO Technical Reports, no view can be expressed as to which approach will be formally adopted. Whilst it could be one or the other, the more likely outcome would be an amalgamation of both.

10.1.10 The present position is brought into sharper focus as the European Commission have recently funded extensive Research on the Benefits of Fire Safety Engineering in the European Union (BeneFEU). It is clear from the conclusions of this Study that in the longer term, a European position will have to be adopted.

10.1.11 There is no doubt that fire safety engineering falls within the scope of the Construction Products Directive (89/106/EEC) and the Interpretative Document (ID2) – Safety in case of fire.

10.1.12 Under the Construction Products Directive (89/106/EEC), the Commission Services have established a Standing Committee on Construction. Reporting to this Standing Committee, the Group of EU Fire Regulators has discussed the issue of fire safety engineering several times. Once a full consideration has been given to the BeneFEU Report, the Fire Regulators Group will need to consider their future options.

10.1.13 At the time of writing, the CEN Technical Committee CEN TC127 – Fire Safety in Buildings, is addressing the need for harmonised technical standards under a direct Standardisation Mandate from the Commission. These technical standards are intended to provide the means of implementing the Essential Requirements of the Directive in respect of reaction to fire and fire resistance testing of construction materials. Thereby providing the European Standards that are needed to make possible the implementation of national laws, regulations and administrative procedures.

10.1.14 It is probable therefore that once the Fire Regulators Group, with the approval of the Standing Committee, have established a 'European' position, the Technical

Committee CEN TC127 may be asked to prepare the European version of the ISO Documents under the existing Mandates.

10.1.15   Any formal European position would take into consideration all published documents on the subject. These would include both the ISO Technical Reports and BS 7974 and the Published Documents. They would also include consideration of any other documents published by any other Member State.

10.2   British Standard BS 7974:2001. Application of fire safety engineering principles to the design of buildings – Code of Practice

10.2.1   This code of practice (BS 7974) is supported by a series (as yet incomplete) of Published Documents: Parts 0–7, that contain guidance and information on how to undertake detailed analysis of specific aspects of fire safety engineering. This does not preclude the use of appropriate methods and data from other sources.

10.2.2   The structure of the code of practice and the Published Documents is given below. This code of practice:

(i)   Provides means of establishing acceptable levels of fire safety economically and without imposing unnecessary constraints on aspects of building design.
(ii)   Provides guidance on the design and assessment of fire safety measures in buildings.
(iii)   Gives a structured approach to assessing the effectiveness of the total fire safety system in achieving the design objectives.
(iv)   Provides a framework for and describes the philosophy of fire safety engineering.
(v)   Outlines the principles involved in the application of the philosophy to the fire safety engineering of particular buildings.
(vi)   Can be used to identify and define one or more fire safety design issues to be addressed using fire safety engineering.
(vii)   Provides some alternative approaches to existing codes and guides for fire safety and also allows the effect of departures from more prescriptive codes to be evaluated.
(viii)   Recognises that a range of alternative and complementary fire protection strategies may achieve the design objectives.

10.2.3   In the Published Documents (PD 7974: Parts 0–7) the following steps in the fire safety design process are identified:

(i)   To define the safety objectives and the scope of the study.
(ii)   To set the acceptance criteria.
(iii)   To characterise the building, occupants and environment.
(iv)   To undertake a qualitative design review.
(v)   To conduct quantified analysis.

10.2.4   The evaluation of the fire safety design of a building is broken down, to simplify the process, into the separate components of the overall system (the sub-systems, see below) belonging to either the tools for fire safety engineering evaluation or the fire safety objectives.

10.3   Structure of Code of Practice BS 7974:2001 – Application of fire safety engineering to the design of buildings

10.3.1   PD 7974-0. Framework and fire safety engineering procedures, content includes:
- Design approach.
- Qualitative Design Review.
- Comparison with criteria.
- Reporting and presentation.

10.3.2   PD 7974-1 (Sub-system 1). Initiation and development of fire within the enclosure of origin, content includes:
- Design approach.
- Acceptance criteria.
- Analysis.
- Data.
- References.

10.3.3   PD 7974-2 (Sub-system 2). Spread of smoke and toxic gases within and beyond the enclosure of origin, content includes:
- Design approach.
- Acceptance criteria.
- Analysis.
- Data.
- References.

10.3.4   PD 7974-3 (Sub-system 3). Structural response and fire spread beyond the enclosure of origin, content includes:
- Design approach.
- Acceptance criteria.
- Analysis.
- Data;
- References.

10.3.5   PD 7974-4 (Sub-system 4). Detection of fire and activation of fire protection systems, content includes:
- Design approach.
- Acceptance criteria.
- Analysis.
- Data.
- References.

10.3.6 PD 7974-5 (Sub-system 5). Fire service intervention, content includes:
- Design approach.
- Acceptance criteria.
- Analysis.
- Data.
- References.

10.3.7 PD 7974-6 (Sub-system 6). (Not yet published, in course of preparation by FSH/24) Evacuation, content includes:
- Design approach.
- Acceptance criteria.
- Analysis.
- Data.
- References.

10.3.8 PD 7974- 7 (Sub-system 7). Probabilistic risk assessment, content includes:
- Design approach.
- Acceptance criteria.
- Analysis.
- Data.
- References.

10.3.9 A brief description of the Scope of each of the sub-systems is given below. There are slight differences in these individual scopes with those of the ISO Technical Report BS ISO/TR 13387.

10.4 Sub-system 1. Initiation and development of fire within the enclosure of origin

10.4.1 Sub-system 1 provides guidance on evaluating fire growth and/or size within the enclosure of origin, as well as enclosures to which the fire has subsequently spread. Guidance is also provided for 'special cases', which include malicious, fires, racked/stacked storage of goods and fires external to the building.

10.4.2 The characteristics of the design fire for any particular scenario are influenced by a number of factors, including building design, environmental influences, potential ignition sources and location, types of combustible materials, distribution and arrangement of combustible materials, ventilation conditions and other events occurring during the fire.

10.4.4 The determination of the characteristics of the design fire from ignition through to decay is used by other sub-systems as inputs into calculations of events such as time of fire spread from enclosure (sub-system 3) and time to activation of fire suppression systems (sub-system 4).

10.5 Sub-system 2. Spread of smoke and toxic gases within and beyond the enclosure of origin

10.5.1   Sub-system 2 provides guidance on the application of fire safety management principles for the treatment of smoke movement, control and management problems. The guidance is intended primarily for professional engineers with a responsibility for the design or assessment of fire safety in buildings.

10.5.2   Sub-system 1 provides information on the rate of production of heat and combustion products from the fire source. The aim of sub-system 2 is to provide design approaches to estimate the spread of the combustion gases within and beyond the room of origin and to evaluate their properties, i.e. temperature, visibility and concentration of toxic products. This information may be used to calculate the time between the detection of a fire and to conditions developing, dangerous to building occupants. This will enable the design of fire safety measures to ensure that sufficient time is available for escape. It also provides information that will allow property issues to be assessed.

10.5.3   Whilst this document forms part of the series of Published Documents containing sub-systems 1 to 7, it may, in consultation with the appropriate references, be regarded as 'stand-alone' guidance.

10.6 Sub-system 3 (PD 7974-3:2003) Structural response and fire spread beyond the enclosure of origin

10.6.1   Sub-system 3 provides guidance and information on how to undertake quantitative and detailed analysis of specific aspects of the design. They are a summary of the state of the art and it is intended that they be updated as new theories, calculation methods and/or data becomes available. They do not preclude the use of appropriate methods and data from other sources.

10.7 Sub-system 4 (PD 7974-4:2003) Detection of fire and activation of fire protection systems

10.7.1   Sub-system 4 provides guidance on the development, design and application of fire detection systems, and the activation of fire alarm and fire control systems to fulfil a role in the fire safety engineered design for a building. Scientific and engineering principles are used as part of a structured approach. The key elements covered are:

● Detection.
● Activation and control.

In the context of this document, fire control includes:

● Fire suppression systems.
● Fire barrier systems.
● Smoke/heat control systems.

10.8   Sub-system 5. Fire service intervention

10.8.1   Sub-system 5 provides guidance on fire service intervention and evaluates the rate of build-up of fire-fighting resources of the fire service. These activities may include in-house or private fire brigades and, in particular the time interval between the call to the local authority fire service and the arrival of the fire service at its predetermined level of attendance. The time interval between the arrival of the fire service and the start of their attack on the fire, the time intervals related to the build-up of any additional fire service resources and the extent of fire-fighting resources and extinguishing capability available at various times.

10.8.2   This sub-system takes information on building characteristics and the design fire from the Qualitative Design Review (QDR), together with the time of fire service notification from sub-system 4 and the time of evacuation from sub-system 6. It provides information on the effect of fire service activities on the growth of the fire, which is used in sub-system 1.

10.9   Sub-system 7. Risk assessment, uncertainty and safety factors

10.9.1   This sub-system provides guidance on probabilistic risk analysis. It sets out the general principles and techniques of risk analysis that can be used in fire safety engineering. This sub-system also outlines the circumstances where this approach is appropriate and gives examples illustrating their use.

10.9.2   The sub-system also includes data for probabilistic risk assessment and criteria for assessment. The data included is based on fire statistics, building characteristics and reliability of fire protection systems. The criteria included cover life safety and property protection, both in absolute and comparative terms.

10.9.3   This sub-system does not contain guidance on techniques for hazard identification or qualitative risk analysis. Probabilistic risk assessment of fire in buildings (with the exception of nuclear, chemical process, offshore and transport) is not widely used and so a discussion of possible future developments is included.

10.10   Technical Reports BS ISO/TR 13387: Parts 1 to 8: 1999

10.10.1   To provide the basis for comparison with BS 7974, a brief synopsis of the ISO Technical Reports follows.

10.10.2   These Technical Reports are relevant to:

(i)   The application of fire performance concepts to design objectives.
(ii)   Design fire scenarios and design fires.
(iii)   Assessment and verification of mathematical fire models.
(iv)   Movement of fire effluents.
(v)   Structural response and fire spread beyond the enclosure of origin.

(vi)   Detection, activation and suppression.

(vii)   Life safety: occupant behaviour, location and condition.

10.10.3   In these Technical Reports, the following important steps in the fire safety design process are identified.

(i)   To define the safety objectives and scope of the study.

(ii)   To set acceptance criteria.

(iii)   To characterise the building, occupants and environment.

(iv)   To undertake a qualitative design review.

(v)   To conduct quantified analysis.

10.10.4   The evaluation of the fire safety design of a building is broken down, to simplify the process, into eight separate components of the system (sub-systems denoted by the prefix SS1 to SS8) belonging either the tools for fire safety engineering evaluation (SS1-5) or the fire safety objectives (SS6-8).

10.11   SS1 Initiation and development of fire and fire effluents

10.11.1   This sub-system provides guidance on the use of engineering methods for the prediction of ignition of fire, the generation of fire effluents, and to the development of fire inside the room of origin.

10.11.2   The sub-system provides a framework for critically reviewing the suitability of an engineering method for assessing the potential for the initiation and development of fire and generation of fire effluents. The sub-system may also provide means to assess the effectiveness of fire safety measures meant to reduce the probability of ignition, to control fire development, and to reduce accumulation of heat, smoke and toxic products or products causing non-thermal damage. Methods for calculating the effects of the design fires for use in the design and assessment of fire safety on a building are also addressed.

10.12   SS2 Movement of fire effluents

10.12.1   This sub-system provides guidance on the use of engineering methods for the prediction of movement of fire effluents in buildings.

10.12.2   The sub-system draws on other sub-systems for the prescription or characterisation of the fire. The prediction of the fire development and the production of fire effluents are provided by sub-system 1. The prediction of the spread of smoke and flames through openings is addressed by sub-system 2 whilst the spread of fire through barriers is provided by sub-system 3.

10.12.3   The sub-system provides a framework for critically reviewing the suitability of an engineering method for assessing the potential for movement of fire effluents during the course of a fire. The sub-system may also provide means to assess the effectiveness of fire safety measures meant to reduce the adverse effects of the movement of fire effluents.

10.13 SS3 Structural response and fire spread beyond the enclosure of origin

10.13.1   This sub-system provides guidance on the use of engineering methods for the prediction of fire spread beyond the enclosure (e.g. room or compartment) of fire origin, to adjacent enclosures within the building, other buildings or external items. The exposure of a building to external fires is also addressed.

10.13.2   The sub-system draws on other sub-systems for a prescription or characterisation of the fire. Sub-system 1, for example, provides prediction of the time to flashover and the temperature history in the room of fire origin. This information, along with the description of the building assemblies (trial design parameters), is employed by the sub-system to predict the likelihood (and time) of fire spread, and the likelihood (and time) of structural collapse.

10.13.3   The sub-system provides a framework for critically reviewing the suitability of an engineering method (hand calculation, computer method or fire test) for assessing the potential for fire spread in a given situation or application. This entails an analysis of the unit physical and chemical processes involved in each of the modes of fire spread (e.g. room to room, building to building). The availability and reliability of the relevant input data for each unit process is also addressed.

10.13.4   Should fire spread from the room or compartment of fire origin or should local structural collapse occur, not only will additional property damage be incurred, but the safety of building occupants and firefighters outside the room or compartment of fire origin can be compromised. Hence data generated by sub-system 3 become input to sub-system 5.

10.13.5   Finally, guidance on interpreting the results of an analysis of the potential of fire spread is also provided. This includes guidance on the selection of criteria for assessing the effectiveness of fire safety measures meant to reduce the potential of fire spread. The latter is only possible if the objectives of fire safety design have been clearly specified.

10.14 SS4 Detection, activation and suppression

10.14.1   This sub-system provides guidance on the use of engineering methods for the prediction of the time to detect smoke or flames by a wide range of commercial devices. This includes the time required for heat sensitive elements in suppression or other control devices to respond to the gas-flow generated by an incipient or growing fire. The sub-system also provides guidance on how to predict, once detection has occurred, the time required to activate the desired response to a fire, such as a alarm, a smoke damper or a specified flow of extinguishing agent from typical distribution devices. Methods to estimate the effectiveness of many common fire-suppression and control strategies are also addressed.

10.14.2   Sub-system 4 draws on sub-systems 1–3 for characterising the size of the fire as well as the temperature, species concentration and gas velocity fields generated by the fire at any time after ignition/initiation of the design fire event. This information, along with a description of sensor location from the building design parameters, is employed by sub-system 4 to predict detection times and the operation of elements, such as those in automatic sprinklers, that allow release of pressurise extinguishing agent (e.g. water) at a nozzle.

10.14.3   The effect of various suppression strategies on the fire heat release rate is estimated in sub-system 4 currently by reference to national codes and installation guidelines and the use of engineering judgement in the application of these guidelines to design fire scenarios. Once an assumed suppression strategy (usually in terms of a required agent flow rate) take effect, there is considerable feedback required between sub-system 4 and sub-system 2 so that the resultant fire environment (e.g. gas temperatures and species concentrations) can be determined. If the fire environment is unacceptable, alternate suppression strategies may have to be considered.

10.14.4   Activation times are also determined in sub-system 4, most often from a wealth of input information available from the manufacturers of the various detection and suppression systems to be installed in a building. The hydraulic design of sprinkler piping system is considered to be part of this activation process since such piping design ensures that the required flow rate of water or other agent will be available when distribution nozzles are activated by the detection elements.

10.15   SS5 Fire service intervention

10.15.1   This sub-system provides guidance on the evaluation of the rate of build-up of fire extinguishing resources of the fire service, including the activities of any in-house or private fire brigades and in particular:

(i)   The time interval between the call to the fire service and the arrival of the fire service pre-determined attendance.

(ii)   The time interval between the arrival of the fire service and the initiation of attack on the fire by the fire service.

(iii) The time intervals related to the build-up of any necessary additional fire service resources.

(iv)   The extent of fire-fighting resources and extinguishing capability available at various times.

10.15.2   The following three sub-systems are the main fire-safety objectives that may need to be addressed in carrying out fire engineering studies. The list is not exhaustive, and not all items may be appropriate to any particular studies.

10.16   SS6 Life, health and safety of people

10.16.1   The occupants of a building and firefighters who may have entered that building together with members of the public, and firefighters who are in the vicinity of the building can, potentially, be put at risk by fire. The main life-safety objectives are therefore to ensure that:

(i)   The occupants are able to remain in place, evacuate to another part of the building or totally evacuate the building without being subject to hazardous (e.g. causing injury or incapacitating) or untenable conditions.

(ii)   Firefighters are safely able to:

(a) assist evacuation where necessary;
(b) effect rescue where necessary;
(c) prevent extensive spread of fire.

(iii)   Collapse of elements of structure does not endanger people (including firefighters) who are likely to be near the building.

10.16.2   Details of life safety strategies and evaluation techniques are given in Annex D of SS6.

10.17   SS7 Property protection

10.17.1   The effects of fire on the continuing viability of a business/infrastructure may be of vital interest and can be substantial and consideration, therefore, should be given to the limitation of damage to:

(i)   The structure and fabric of the system (building).
(ii)   The contents of the system.
(iii)   Ongoing business/activity viability.
(iv)   Public perception or image.

10.18   SS8 Environmental protection

10.18.1   A fire involving several buildings or the release of quantities of hazardous materials may have an environmental impact that is out of all proportion to the size of the original fire. A small fire involving some toxic products extinguished by water that goes into an adjacent river may lead to large or extensive environmental pollution. Consideration should, therefore, be given to the limitation of:

(i)   The effects of fire on adjacent buildings or facilities.
(ii)   The release of hazardous materials into the environment.

Chapter 11 – Technical Standards in support of Fire Safety Engineering

11.1 Introduction

11.1.1 Much of the guidance given in this document is expressed in terms of performance in relation to British and European Standards for products or methods of test or design. Previous guidance has been given in terms of British Standards only, but with the introduction of the Construction Products Directive (89/106/EEC) and the associated standardisation Mandates awarded to the European Standards Body (CEN), this has changed.

11.1.2 Within CEN rules, the publication of a CEN technical standard, whether or not it is a harmonised standard, i.e. a reference to the technical standard being published in the Official Journal of the European Union, requires that any conflicting national standard should be withdrawn.

11.1.3 With the publication of such technical standards, it is usual practice for the national Standards Body, British Standards in the case of the United Kingdom, to dual number the standard so giving it the full authority and status of a British Standard. Such technical standards will carry the prefix of BS EN xxxx. Where the technical standard has been produced by the International Standards Organisation (ISO) under a Vienna Agreement and subsequently adopted by CEN, it will be designated as BS EN ISO xxxx.

11.1.4 A fundamental aspect of the preparation and subsequent evaluation of an engineered solution to the fire safety requirements in any building, is the use of agreed technical standards. The data supplied by the use of all such technical standards is crucial to the calculations intended to provide the basis of any engineered solution.

11.1.5 The Construction Products Directive (89/106/EEC) provides the basic need for all such technical standards and, in order to achieve the speedy preparation of the requisite technical standards, the Commission Services provided a Standardisation Mandate to the European Standards Body (CEN). This Mandate (M/109) provides the formal request to the European Standards Body to prepare all the necessary technical standards covering:

(i)   Fire behaviour of construction products

(ii)   Fire detection/alarm systems

(iii)   Fire and smoke control products

(iv)   Fixed fire-fighting systems

in support of the Construction Products Directive (89/106/EEC).

11.1.6   The Construction Products Directive will now be able to provide for all construction products to be re-classified using a new set of common test methods. These products are currently controlled by national building regulations, using classifications derived from national test methods in each Member State. The United Kingdom Regulations use test methods described in the BS 476 series.

11.1.7   For a short time (transitional period) it will be possible for each Member State (including the United Kingdom) to continue to use products already classified using the existing national tests alongside the new test methods.

11.1.8   This route may be unattractive to manufacturers and suppliers as the existing classification will only be applicable to the Member State concerned, e.g. materials classified by the UK national test will only be used in the UK. Any materials of products classified using the new harmonised test methods on the other hand, can be sold anywhere in the EEA.

11.1.9   It is expected that the use of the new harmonised test methods (and possibly the classification system) will be much wider that the Member States. Suppliers, particularly from the neighbouring non-European Union countries, who trade extensively with this large market, will also have to work with these methods of test and classification.

11.1.10   The Commission Services recently defined the criteria for assessing building products (Guidance Paper G). This assessment placed construction products into two sets – the major group of all construction products, except flooring and the second set applicable to flooring only. Following the issue of the Guidance Papers, the Commission Services were able to come to two formal Decisions. The Commission Decision 2000/367/CEC set out a European classification system for resistance to fire performance for construction projects. The Commission Decision 2000/147/CEC set out a similar classification system for reaction to fire classification for construction products.

11.1.11   Products are classified into the principle classes of A1, A2, B, C and D after testing with the harmonised test methods (see below). Most of the tests are common to both product groups.

11.1.12   Products in the major group (non-flooring) are tested using all the test methods, which includes BS EN 13823, thermal attack by a single burning item (SBI). Flooring is not tested using this apparatus, BS EN ISO 9239 is used instead.

11.1.13   The main classification criteria for all construction products, other than flooring materials is given in the Guidance Paper G.

11.1.14   Products in class A1 are mostly based on traditionally 'non-combustible' materials and classification into this group is gained by testing using BS EN 1716 and BS EN 1182 (see below).

11.1.15   Classification into classes A2, B, C, and D which are the major classes inhabited by most products, other than those in class A1 and classified as non-combustible. The full listing of the technical standards and the associated performance requirements of all the classes is given in Tables 1 and 2.

11.2   Technical Standards

11.2.1   It is now clear, that given the very wide range of technical standards developed in response to this Mandate (see below), that there is very little in the way of general fire safety that is not subjected to an appropriate technical standard.

11.2.2   The transposition of these technical standards into national standards by the Member States national standards bodies provides for a harmonised approach to the specification and control of fire safety measures. The publication of such standards and the appropriate performance levels allows, in the case of construction products, products to be specified in accordance with the European Classification System as published by the Commission Services in Guidance Paper 'G' concerning the Construction Products Directive – 89/106/EEC.

11.2.3   This Guidance Paper addresses issues relating to the functioning of the European system for the classification of reaction to fire performance of construction products (Euroclasses, within the context of the implementation of the Construction Products Directive.

11.2.4   Arrangements for the transition from existing national classifications for fire performance to the new European systems are dealt with in Guidance Paper 'J' issued by the Commission Services under the provisions of The Construction Products Directive (89/106/EEC).

11.2.5   In the context of this Guidance Paper, 'transitional arrangements' refers to the time period during which national and European technical specifications are both available for use by producers placing their products on the EEA market – the period of co-existence.

11.2.6   The main objective of co-existence is to allow producers to adapt gradually to the conformity assessment procedures and the essential requirements set up by the Directive.

11.3 List of Technical Standards (Euronorms)

11.3.1 The following technical standards have been developed under the formal Mandate M/109 concerning the execution of standardisation work for harmonised standards on the subject categories listed.

11.4 Fire Behaviour of Construction Products

Fire resistance tests (replacing BS 476:Parts 20:21:22:23 & 24)

BS EN 13501: Part 1 – Fire classification of construction products and building elements. Classification using test data from reaction to fire tests.

BS EN 13501: Part 2 – Fire classification of construction products and building elements. Classification using test data from fire resistance test.

BS EN 13501: Part 3 – Fire classification of construction products and building elements. Classification using test data from fire resistance tests on components of normal building services installations.

BS EN 13501: Part 4 – Classification using data from fire resistance tests on smoke control systems.

BS EN 13501: Part 5 – Classification using data from external fire exposure to roof tests.

BS EN 1363: Part 1 – Fire resistance tests; general requirements.

BS EN 1363: Part 2 – Fire resistance tests, alternative and additional procedures.

BS EN 1363: Part 3 – Fire resistance tests, verification of furnace performance.

BS EN 1364: Part 1 – Fire resistance tests for non-load bearing elements, walls.

BS EN 1364: Part 2 – Fire resistance tests for non-load bearing elements, ceilings.

BS EN 1364: Part 3 – Fire resistance tests for non-load bearing elements, curtain walls, full configuration.

BS EN 1364: Part 4 – Fire resistance tests for non-load bearing elements, curtain walls, part configuration.

BS EN 1364: Part 5 – Fire resistance tests for non-load bearing elements, semi-natural fire tests for facades and curtain walls.

BS EN 1365: Part 1 – Fire resistance tests for load bearing elements, walls.

BS EN 1365: Part 2 – Fire resistance tests for load bearing elements, floors and roofs.

BS EN 1365: Part 3 – Fire resistance tests for load bearing elements, beams.

BS EN 1365: Part 4 – Fire resistance tests for load bearing elements, columns.

BS EN 1365: Part 5 – Fire resistance tests for load bearing elements, balconies.

BS EN 1365: Part 6 – Fire resistance tests for load bearing elements, stairs and walkways.

BS EN 1366: Part 1 – Fire resistance tests for service installations, ducts.

BS EN 1366: Part 2 – Fire resistance tests for service installations, fire dampers.

BS EN 1366: Part 3 – Fire resistance tests for service installations, penetration seals.

BS EN 1366: Part 4 – Fire resistance tests for service installations, linear joint seals.

BS EN 1366: Part 5 – Fire resistance tests for service installations, service ducts and shafts.

BS EN 1366: Part 6 – Fire resistance tests for service installations, raised floors.

BS EN 1366: Part 7 – Fire resistance tests for service installations, closures for conveyors and track bound systems.

BS EN 1366: Part 8 – Fire resistance tests for service installations, smoke extraction ducts.

BS EN 1366: Part 9 – Fire resistance tests for service installations, single compartment smoke extraction ducts.

BS EN 1366: Part 10 – Fire resistance tests for service installations, smoke control dampers.

BS EN 1634: Part 1 – Fire resistance tests for door and shutter assemblies, fire doors.

BS EN 1634: Part 2 – Fire resistance tests for door and shutter assemblies, fire door hardware.

BS EN 1634: Part 3 – Fire resistance tests for door and shutter assemblies, smoke control doors.

Reaction to fire tests (replacing BS 476; Parts 4;6;7 & 11)

BS EN ISO 1182 – Reaction to fire tests for building products, non-combustibility test.

BS EN ISO 1716 – Reaction to fire tests for building products, determination of calorific value.

BS EN 11925:Part 2 – Reaction to fire tests for building products, ignitability when subjected to direct flame impingement.

BS EN 13823 – Reaction to fire tests for building products – building products, excluding flooring exposed to the thermal attack by a single burning item (SBI).

BS EN 13238 – Reaction to fire tests for building products – conditioning procedures and general rules for selection of substrates.

BS EN 13501: Part 1 – Fire classification of construction products and building elements, classification using data from reaction to fire tests.

11.5   Fire detection and fire alarm systems

BS EN 54: Part 1 – Fire detection and fire alarm systems. Introduction.

BS EN 54: Part 2 – Fire detection and fire alarm systems. Control and indicating equipment.

BS EN 54: Part 3 – Fire detection and fire alarm systems. Fire alarm devices. Sounders.

BS EN 54: Part 4 – Fire detection and fire alarm systems. Power supply equipment.

BS EN 54: Part 5 – Fire detection and fire alarm systems. Point detectors.

BS EN 54: Part 6 – Fire detection and fire alarm systems. Point detectors using scattered light, transmitted light or ionisation.

BS EN 54: Part 10 – Fire detection and fire alarm systems. Flame detectors. Point detectors.

BS EN 54: Part 11 – Fire detection and fire alarm systems. Manual call points.

11.6 Smoke and heat control systems

BS EN 12101: Part 1 – Smoke and heat control systems. Specification for smoke curtains. Requirements and test methods.
BS EN 12101: Part 2 – Smoke and heat control systems. Specification for natural smoke and heat exhaust ventilators.
BS EN 12101: Part 3 – Smoke and heat control systems. Specification for powered smoke and heat exhaust ventilators.
BS EN 12101: Part 4 – Smoke and heat control systems. Fire and smoke control installation. Kits.
BS EN 12101: Part 6 – Smoke and heat control systems. Functional requirements and calculations methods, components and procedures.

11.7 Fixed fire-fighting systems

BS EN 12259: Part 1 – Fixed fire-fighting systems. Components for sprinkler and water spray systems. Sprinklers.
BS EN 12259: Part 2 – Fixed fire-fighting systems. Components for sprinkler and water spray systems. Wet alarm valve assemblies.
BS EN 12259: Part 3 – Fixed fire-fighting systems. Components from sprinkler and water spray systems. Dry alarm valve assemblies.
BS EN 12259: Part 4 – Fixed fire-fighting systems. Components from sprinkler and water spray systems. Water motor alarms.
BS EN 12259: Part 5 – Fixed fire-fighting systems. Components from sprinkler and water spray systems. Water flow detectors.
BS EN 12259: Part 9 – Fixed fire-fighting systems. Components from sprinkler and water spray systems. Deluge valves.
BS EN 12259: Part 10 – Fixed fire-fighting systems. Components from sprinkler and water spray systems. Multiple controls.
BS EN 12259: Part 11 – Fixed fire-fighting systems. Components from sprinkler and water spray systems. Medium and high velocity water spray.
BS EN 12259: Part 12 – Fixed fire-fighting systems. Components from sprinkler and water spray systems. Sprinkler pumps.

11.8 Fixed fire-fighting systems. Components for gas extinguishing systems

BS EN 12094: Part 1 – Fixed fire-fighting systems. Components for gas extinguishing systems. Requirements and test methods for electrical automatic control and delay devices.
BS EN 12094: Part 2 – Fixed fire-fighting systems. Components for gas extinguishing systems. Requirements and test methods for non-electric apparatus.
BS EN 12094: Part 3 – Fixed fire-fighting systems. Components for gas extinguishing systems. Requirements and test methods for manual triggering and stop devices.
BS EN 12094: Part 4 – Fixed fire-fighting systems. Components for gas extinguishing systems. Requirements and test methods for high-pressure container valve assemblies and their actuators.

BS EN 12094: Part 5 – Fixed fire-fighting systems. Components for gas extinguishing systems. Requirements and test methods for high and low pressure selector valves and their actuators for CO_2 systems.

BS EN 12094: Part 6 – Fixed fire-fighting systems. Components for gas extinguishing systems. Requirements and test methods for non-electrical disable devices for CO_2 systems.

BS EN 12094: Part 7 – Fixed fire-fighting systems. Components for gas extinguishing systems. Requirements and test methods for nozzles for CO_2 systems.

BS EN 12094: Part 8 – Fixed fire-fighting systems. Components for gas extinguishing systems. Requirements and test methods for flexible connectors for CO_2 systems.

BS EN 12094: Part 9 – Fixed fire-fighting systems. Components for gas extinguishing systems. Requirements and test methods for special fire detectors.

BS EN 12094: Part 10 – Fixed fire-fighting systems. Components for gas extinguishing systems. Requirements and test methods for pressure gauges and pressure devices.

BS EN 12094: Part 11 – Fixed fire-fighting systems. Components for gas extinguishing systems. Requirements and test methods for mechanical weighing devices.

BS EN 12094: Part 12 – Fixed fire-fighting systems. Components for gas extinguishing systems. Requirements and test methods for mechanical alarm devices.

BS EN 12094: Part 13 – Fixed fire-fighting systems. Components for gas extinguishing systems. Requirements and test methods for non-return valves.

BS EN 12094: Part 16 – Fixed fire-fighting systems. Components for gas extinguishing systems. Requirements and test methods odorising devices for CO_2 low pressure systems.

11.9 Fixed fire-fighting systems. Powder systems

BS EN 12416: Part 2 – Fixed fire-fighting systems. Powder systems. Design, construction and maintenance.

11.10 Fixed fire-fighting systems. Automatic sprinkler systems

BS EN 12845 – Fixed fire-fighting systems. Automatic spinkler systems. Design and installation.

11.11 Other, non-mandated technical standards

11.11.1   In addition to the above technical standards produced under the Mandate M/109, other products now covered by technical standards that are relevant cover the manufacture of portable fire extinguishers. A list of the appropriate technical standards is given below:

11.12   Portable fire extinguishers

BS EN 3: Part 1 – Portable fire extinguishers. Description, duration of operation, class A and B fire test.

BS EN 3: Part 2 – Portable fire extinguishers. Tightness, dielectric test, tamping test, special provisions.

BS EN 3: Part 3 – Portable fire extinguishers. Construction, resistance to pressure, mechanical tests.

BS EN 3: Part 4 – Portable fire extinguishers. Charges, minimum required fire.

BS EN 3: Part 5 – Portable fire extinguishers. Specification and supplementary tests.

BS EN 3: Part 6 – Portable fire extinguishers. Provisions for the attestation of conformity of portable fire extinguishers in accordance with BS EN 3 Part 1 to Part 5.

11.13   Extended Application of Test Methods

11.13.1   The basic test methods given above apply, by direct application to the construction materials specified in the title and scope of the technical standard. This direct application imposes a substantial cost penalty on the material producers who are faced with the requirement to test every product for its fire performance.

11.13.2   This requirement is applied in the case of any change or modification to the material specification and it is this requirement that imposes the financial burden.

11.13.3   Within CEN Technical Committee TC127 therefore, a procedure of what is termed 'Extended Application' is applied. Under the extended application procedures or rules certain, limited changes are permitted to the material specification.

11.13.4   The general rules and procedures of extended application are still being developed but many material producers are seeking to apply such practices already.

Appendix 1 – Tables

Table 1: Classes of Reaction to Fire Performance for Construction Products, excluding Floorings

Notes to Table 1

Table 2: Classes of Reaction to Fire Performance for Floorings

Notes to Table 2

Table 1: *Classes of Reaction to Fire Performance for Construction Products, Excluding Floorings*

Class	Test method(s)	Classification criteria	Additional classification
A1	EN ISO 1182: 2002 [1]; and	$\Delta T \leq 30°C$; and $\Delta m \leq 50\%$; and $t_f = 0$ (i.e. no sustained flaming)	
	EN ISO 1716: 2002	$PCS \leq 2,0$ MJ/kg [1] and $PCS \leq 2,0$ MJ/kg [2] [2a] and $PCS \leq 1,4$ MJ/m^2 [3] and $PCS \leq 2,0$ MJ/kg [4]	
A2	EN ISO 1182: 2002 [1]; or	$\Delta T \leq 50°C$; and $\Delta m \leq 50\%$; and $t_f \leq 20s$	
	EN ISO 1716: 2002 and	$PCS \leq 3,0$ MJ/kg [1] and $PCS \leq 4,0$ MJ/m^2 [2] and $PCS \leq 4,0$ MJ/m^2 [3] and $PCS \leq 3,0$ MJ/kg [4]	
	EN 13823: 2002	$FIGRA \leq 120$ W/s; and LFS < edge of specimen; and $THR_{600s} \leq 7,5$ MJ	Smoke production [5]; and Flaming droplets/particles [6]
B	EN 13823: 2002	$FIGRA \leq 120$ W/s; and LFS < edge of specimen; and $THR_{600s} \leq 7,5$ MJ	Smoke production [5]; and Flaming droplets/particles [6]
	EN ISO 11925-2: 2002 [8]: Exposure = 30s	$Fs \leq 150mm$ within 60s	
C	EN 13823: 2002 and	$FIGRA \leq 250$ W/s; and LFS < edge of specimen; and $THR_{600s} \leq 15$ MJ	Smoke production [5]; and Flaming droplets/particles [6]
	prEN ISO 11925-2: 1998 [8]: Exposure = 30s	$Fs \leq 150mm$ within 60s	
D	EN 13823: 2002 and	$FIGRA \leq 750$ W/s	Smoke production [5]; and Flaming droplets/particles [6]
	EN ISO 11925-2: 2002 [8]: Exposure = 30s	$Fs \leq 150mm$ within 60s	
E	prEN ISO 11925-2: 1998 [8]: Exposure = 15s	$Fs \leq 150mm$ within 20s	Flaming droplets/particles [7]
F		No performance determined	

Notes to Table 1

[1]   For homogeneous products and substantial components of non-homogeneous products

[2]   For any external non-substantial component of non-homogeneous products

[2a]   Alternatively, any external non-substantial component having a PCS $< 2,0$ MJ/m^2, provided that the product satisfies the following criteria of
EN 13823, FIGRA < 20 W/s, and
LFS $<$ edge of specimen, and
THR$_{600s}$ $< 4,0$ MJ, and
s1, and
d0

[3]   For any internal non-substantial component of non-homogeneous products

[4]   For the product as a whole

[5]   In the last phase of the development of the test procedure, modifications of the smoke measurement system have been introduced, the effect of which needs further investigation. This may result in a modification of the limit values and/or parameters for the evaluation of the smoke production.
s1 = SMOGRA ≤ 30m^2/s^2 and TSP$_{600s}$ ≤ 50m^2;
s2 = SMOGRA ≤ 180m^2/s^2 and TSP$_{600s}$ ≤ 200m^2;
s3 = not s1 or s2

[6]   **d0** = No flaming droplets/ particles in EN 13823(SBI) within 600s;
d1 = No flaming droplets/ particles persisting longer than 10s in EN13823 (SBI) within 600s;
d2 = not d0 or d1;
Ignition of the paper in EN ISO 11925-2 results in a d2 classification

[7]   Pass = no ignition of the paper (no classification);
Fail = ignition of the paper (**d2** classification)

[8]   Under conditions of surface flame attack and, if appropriate to the end-use application of the product, edge flame attack.

Table 2: *Classes of Reaction to Fire Performance for Floorings*

Class	Test method(s)	Classification criteria	Additional classification
$A1_{fl}$	EN ISO 1182: 2002 [1]; and	$\Delta T \leq 30°C$; and $\Delta m \leq 50\%$; and $t_f = 0$ (i.e. no sustained flaming)	
	EN ISO 1716: 2002	$PCS \leq 2{,}0$ MJ/kg [1] and $PCS \leq 2{,}0$ MJ/kg [2] [2a] and $PCS \leq 1{,}4$ MJ/m^2 [3] and $PCS \leq 2{,}0$ MJ/kg [4]	
$A2_{fl}$	EN ISO 1182: 2002 [1]; or	$\Delta T \leq 50°C$; and $\Delta m \leq 50\%$; and $t_f \leq 20s$	
	EN ISO 1716: 2002 and	$PCS \leq 3{,}0$ MJ/kg [1] and $PCS \leq 4{,}0$ MJ/m^2 [2] and $PCS \leq 4{,}0$ MJ/m^2 [3] and $PCS \leq 3{,}0$ MJ/kg [4]	
	EN ISO 9239-1: 2002 [5]	Critical flux [6] $\geq 8{,}0$ kW/m^2	Smoke production [7]
B_{fl}	EN ISO 9239-1: 2002 [5] and	Critical flux [6] $\geq 8{,}0$ kW/m^2	Smoke production [7]
	EN ISO 11925-2: 2002 Exposure = 15s	Fs ≤ 150mm within 20s	
C_{fl}	EN ISO 9239-1: 2002 [5] and	Critical flux [6] $\geq 4{,}5$ kW/m^2	Smoke production [7]
	EN ISO 11925-2: 2002 [8] Exposure = 15s	Fs ≤ 150mm within 20s	
D_{fl}	EN ISO 9239-1: 2002 [5] and	Critical flux [6] $\geq 3{,}0$ kW/m^2	Smoke production [7]
	EN ISO 11925-2: 2002 [8] Exposure = 15s	Fs ≤ 150mm within 20s	
E_{fl}	EN ISO 11925-2: 2002 Exposure = 15s	Fs ≤ 150mm within 20s	
F_{fl}		No performance determined	

Notes to Table 2

[1]   For homogeneous products and substantial components of non-homogeneous products

[2]   For any external non-substantial component of non-homogeneous products

[3]   For any internal non-substantial component of non-homogeneous products

[4]   For the product as a whole

[5]   Test duration = 30 minutes

[6]   Critical flux is defined as the radiant flux at which the flame extinguishes or the radiant flux after a test period of 30 minutes, whichever is the lower (i.e. the flux corresponding with the furthest extent of spread of flame).

[7]   **s1** = Smoke $\leq$ 750%.min;

       s2 = not s1

[8]   Under conditions of surface flame attack and, if appropriate to the end use application of the product, edge flame attack.

Glossary of Terms

Available safe egress time (ASET)

Calculated time available between ignition of a fire and the time at which tenability criteria are exceeded in a specified space in a building.

Escape time

Calculated time from ignition until the time at which all of the occupants of a specified part of the building are able to reach a place of safety.

Deterministic study

Methodology based upon physical relationships derived from scientific theories and empirical results, which for a given set of initial conditions will always produce the same outcome.

Equivalence

In respect of a fire safety requirement, the provision by other means of a level of safety providing the same level of performance as that referred to in guidance relevant to that requirement.

Evacuation time

Interval between the time of warning of fire being transmitted to the occupants and the time at which all of the occupants are able to reach a place of safety.

Fire Hazard

Source of possible injury or damage from fire.

Fire Risk

Product of probability of occurrence of a fire to be expected in a given technical operation or state in a defined time, and the consequence or extent of damage to be expected on the occurrence of a fire.

Fire Safety Engineer

Person suitably qualified and experienced in fire safety engineering.

Fire Safety Engineering

The application of scientific and engineering principles to the protection of people, property and the environment from fire.

Functional Requirement

The expression of a safety requirement in terms of the required level of performance of the fire safety system referred to.

Probabilistic risk assessment

Methodology to determine statistically the probability and outcome of events.

Prescriptive Requirement

The expression of a safety requirement by means of a detailed description the provisions required which should not be varied.

Science

The observation, identification, description, experimental investigation and theoretical explanation of phenomena.

Trial fire safety design

Package of fire safety measures, which in the context of the building may meet the specified fire safety objectives.

Acknowledgements

HM Fire Service Inspectorate is indebted to all who helped with the provision of information and expertise to assist the production of this Manual, in particular:

Professor SD Christian PhD MPhil
FireSERT
University of Ulster